THE GOLDEN PLEASURE BOOK OF

BIOLOGY

A COLOURFUL INTRODUCTION TO THE WONDER OF LIFE

BY GERALD AMES AND ROSE WYLER AND ILLUSTRATED BY CHARLES HARPER

PAUL HAMLYN · LONDON

Foreword

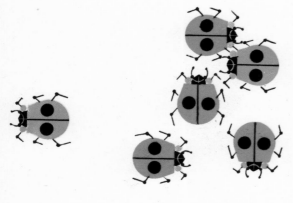

Life was bound to come, though it took a long time.

Our world began about 5,000 million years ago. The sun is about that old, and the earth only a little younger. The oldest rocks on the earth are less than 3,000 million years old; it seems to have taken almost 2,000 million years for the crust of the earth to settle down enough to hold rocks in place. In some very old rocks, almost 2,000 million years old, fossils have lately been discovered, the remains of microscopic creatures, some perhaps already capable of using the energy of sunlight to make their food. Life had started on its long exploration of this planet, almost surely in the sea, where it remained for many ages.

About 400 million years ago, plants and a few animals emerged on to the land, the plants of course before the animals, since how otherwise could the animals have managed? Soon afterwards the first lung-breathers, the first amphibia, crawled out upon the land; and then, about 200 million years ago, descendants of these, the reptiles, became the lords of creation. Within another 50 million years, out of the reptiles came the first warm-blooded creatures, the birds and mammals. Then, for reasons still not well understood, the great reptiles vanished, and the warm-blooded animals inherited the earth. About 1 million years ago, some of them began to be human, and about 50,000 years ago one such creature came to be our kind of man. And here you are, 50,000 years later, with a book that tells the story.

Scientists have taken lately to asking a strange riddle, a little for the fun of it: "Why is the world 5,000 million years old?" It has a strange answer: "Because it took 5,000 million years to reach a creature that would ask."

You are that creature, that new thing in the world, the creature that asks questions, that wants to know. This book should help. I learned a lot from it, though I have been a scientist and teacher for many years; so you may learn a lot from it too. It isn't just a child's book, whatever that might mean. All of us who are scientists know that it is the questions children ask that are the hardest to answer. Most grown-ups stop asking those questions after a time, not because they have learned the answers, but because they have stopped trying. The ones who keep on asking are the great scientists. They are a kind of learned boy—or girl. There is nothing better.

I knew I would like this book when I read on the first page: "Questions are just as important as answers." Science is a way of asking more and more meaningful questions. The answers are important mainly in leading us to new questions. So try to learn some answers, because they are useful and interesting; but don't forget that it isn't answers that make a scientist, it's questions.

GEORGE WALD
Professor of Biology, Harvard University

First published 1962
Second impression 1963

Published by Paul Hamlyn Ltd., Westbook House, Fulham Broadway, London, for
Golden Pleasure Books Ltd. by arrangement with Golden Press Inc.
© Copyright Golden Press Inc., 1961
Printed in Czechoslovakia

T 1202

CONTENTS

Billions of Living Things...and You

If a stone could talk, and asked you what it is like to be alive, what would you say? You might say that your heart beats, and that you breathe and grow.

But such an answer just leads to other questions. What is a heart-beat? Answer: a pumping action that sends blood through your arteries and veins. Your heart beats about 70 times a minute, 100,800 times a day, 37 million times a year. In ten years, it pumps enough blood to float a ship. But why is all this pumping of blood necessary to keep you alive?

Questions are just as important as answers. Growth seems ordinary and commonplace, until you stop to think about it. "How you've grown!" friends of the family say. Then they go on to talk about something else. Plants and animals grow; you

are expected to do the same. But stones and dead things don't grow; why is it that living things do?

The minute you ask this question, growth seems wonderful and amazing.

Plants and Animals Almost Everywhere

Think of all the different kinds of living things in the world. Cats and dogs, elms and oaks, birds and insects, ferns and mushrooms, spiders and elephants—you could go on and on naming them, for there are more than a million different kinds of living things.

Creatures of some sort live almost everywhere in the world. Strange fishes swim in the depths of the

5

sea. Some live five miles below the surface. Nets have been dragged through the deep sea, and sometimes have brought up fishes and other living things.

Many kinds of fishes from the deep sea are blind. Eyes would not be very useful to them, for the deep sea is darker than night. Instead of seeing, these fishes smell and feel their way through the water. But other fishes do have eyes, and also spots that glow. They find one another in the dark by their glimmering spots.

While some creatures live five miles down in the sea, others drift five miles up in the air. You would not think these drifting things were alive. They are little dry flecks, so small they can be seen only under a microscope. If they settle to earth and fall in a moist place, the flecks turn into tiny animals and plants.

What a marvellous assortment of creatures populate the earth! Giants like whales and massive oak trees, and tiny plants and animals that can't be seen with the naked eye. So many different sizes and shapes! A thousand science-fiction writers couldn't imagine them all.

You would almost think that living things could be practically any size and shape. In ages past, people believed they could. But in those times there were all kinds of strange beliefs. People thought that toads and mice came from mud, and that salamanders lived in fire.

Today we know these old ideas are nonsense. We realise that the way to study living things is to find out what they are made of, how their bodies work, and how they manage to exist in their homes.

The Science of Life

To investigate a million kinds of living things is a huge task. So the study of life is divided into several branches. Experts in each of them do different work, but they all help to build up one great science of life – biology.

Biology is full of surprises. As you learn its secrets, you find out how plants and animals keep alive and grow. And not only that. You see how you yourself are like every other creature in some ways, but different in others. You discover just where you fit among the world's billions of living things.

6

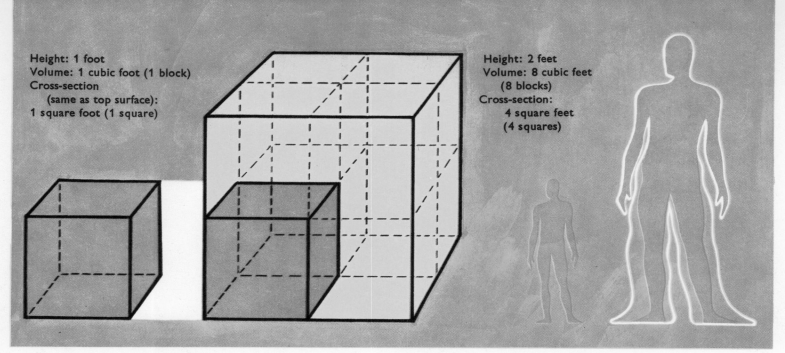

Height: 1 foot
Volume: 1 cubic foot (1 block)
Cross-section
    (same as top surface):
1 square foot (1 square)

Height: 2 feet
Volume: 8 cubic feet
    (8 blocks)
Cross-section:
    4 square feet
    (4 squares)

A giant twice as tall as an ordinary man would need legs 8 times as large in cross-section

The Very Great, The Very Small

Living things aren't put together in just any fashion. They are built according to definite plans.

Take yourself, for example. You are growing, but you won't become twenty feet tall. And this is fortunate. A person twenty feet tall would have a terrible problem just trying to stand up.

The Giant's Problem

If you have read *Gulliver's Travels*, you remember the adventures of Gulliver in the land called Brobdingnag. The people there are giants many times taller than Gulliver, but their general shape and proportions are like his. For example, their legs are quite thick, but no thicker than Gulliver's in proportion to their height.

Could such creatures really exist? Perhaps Jonathan Swift, who wrote the story, didn't care whether they could or not. Or perhaps he just forgot a certain mathematical law. This law says that if two bodies are similar in shape but one is twice the height of the other, the larger body will be eight times as bulky and heavy as the smaller. The drawings of the two blocks show how this works.

The larger block is exactly twice the height, width, and thickness of the smaller one. This makes its volume eight times the volume of the smaller figure. Now notice another thing—the cross-section. This is the surface you would get by cutting one of the blocks across the middle. It is the same as the top surface. In the larger block, the cross-section is only four times that of the smaller one —not eight times, like the volume. What would this mean in the case of a giant?

Imagine what would happen to a full-grown man if his height were doubled and he became a giant, but his proportions stayed the same. The giant's volume would be eight times greater, and this would mean he would be eight times heavier. But the cross-section of his leg would be only four times greater —that is, it would have increased only half as much as his weight.

This would be bad for the giant, since the strength of bone and muscle depends on their cross-section. The giant's legs would be only half as strong as needed. If his legs were to have strength in proportion to his weight, their cross-section would have to become eight times greater when his height doubled. And if he grew as tall as a Brobdingnagian, he would need legs like tree trunks! Otherwise he couldn't even stand. The earth's gravity would pull him down with terrible crushing force.

8

When It's Good to be Small

Once a man carelessly dropped a mouse from a skyscraper window. It drifted gently to the ground and landed unharmed. Why? Because of nature's law about volume and surface.

The law works like this. Suppose there are two creatures of similar shape, and one is half the length of the other. Then the volume of the smaller one will be one-eighth that of the larger. You can prove this from the blocks on the opposite page. The weight of the smaller, like its volume, will be one-eighth that of the larger. But its surface area will be one-quarter that of the larger. So a small creature has a large surface for its volume and weight. This is what helped the falling mouse. Air striking against its large surface slowed the fall.

An animal as small as a mouse does have another problem—keeping its balance. A wind might easily blow it over if it were tall and long-legged. But the mouse has short legs and a low-slung body, so he doesn't topple and tumble around.

For a still smaller creature, something more is needed. Notice how a spider's legs spread out. This helps the spider to keep its balance. Great strength is needed to support a body on spreading legs. But a spider has the strength—because it is small.

Suppose there are two insects, and one is half the size of the other. The smaller one's weight will be one-eighth that of the larger, but it will have muscles one-quarter as large in cross-section, and this makes the smaller one twice as strong for its weight.

Compare the flea and the grasshopper. The little flea is a better jumper. The grasshopper can jump thirty times its length; the flea, two hundred times!

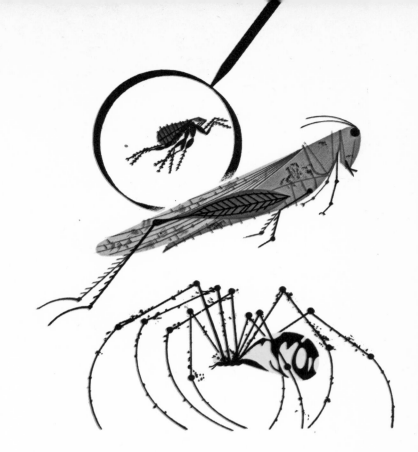

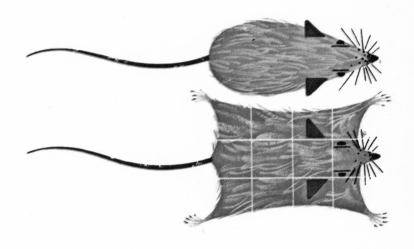

The **flea** and **grasshopper** (above); the garden spider

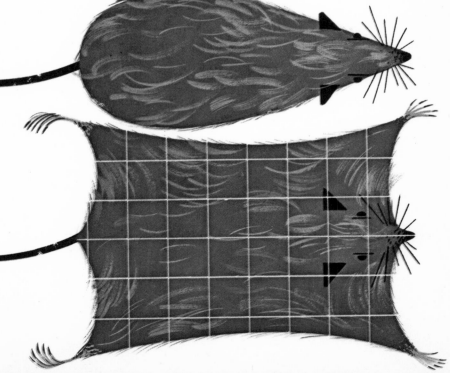

Surface and Volume. The length of the mouse is $1/2$ that of the rat. Its volume is $1/8$. Its surface area is $1/4$. It has a larger surface than the rat in proportion to volume

Size in the Sea

In the great realm of the sea drift billions of green or yellow specks that can't be seen with the naked eye. They are plants, and need light in order to live. This means they must remain within a few hundred feet of the surface, where the water is well lighted. Beneath that level is twilight; and beneath that, darkness.

Because living substance is just a bit heavier than water, a sea plant is always in danger of sinking into the dark. It depends mainly on its small size to keep afloat. Like any tiny thing, the plant has a large surface for its volume. As it begins to sink, its surface rubs against the water. The greater the surface, the greater the friction, and the slower the sinking.

Floating Meadows

Billions of plants do finally sink into the dark and die. But others are carried upward by currents. They remain in the lighted water, where they grow and multiply, and make floating meadows that sometimes colour the sea green.

To live and grow, plants need several kinds of dissolved substances called nutrients. Some of these are many thousands of times scarcer in the ocean than in good soil. During seasons when the ocean plants grow and multiply rapidly, the scarce nutrients are almost completely used up. Then there is famine in the sea. The little plants stop increasing, and nearly die out.

Under such conditions, small size gives a big advantage. In the first place, a tiny plant needs only small amounts of nutrients. In the second place, it has a large surface for its volume. All nutrients come through the surface, so plenty can be taken in.

Tiny sea plants are the food of hordes of little animals. Most of these are so small that they can barely be seen with the naked eye. The most numerous kind, the oar-feet or copepods, swim along waving little fringed nets with which they catch the plants.

Tiny plant-eaters are eaten by small fishes, and these in turn by larger fishes and other animals. All the ocean's creatures, from copepods to whales, owe their lives to the microscopic plants, whose small size enables them to thrive in the sea.

Microscopic plants and animals that float in the sunlit waters of the sea

The microscope used by Anthony van Leeuwenhoek
to study the world's smallest animals

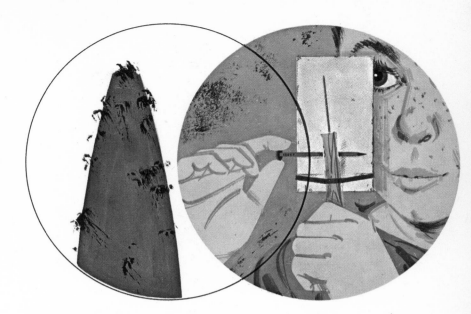

A home-made microscope with a water-drop lens makes
a needle look like a spike

Hunting With a Microscope

Three hundred years ago, before there were microscopes, people never even dreamed that hordes of tiny creatures lived all around them. Then, in the city of Delft, in Holland, Anthony van Leeuwenhoek made a microscope, and with it discovered a new world.

Leeuwenhoek was a cloth merchant, and often used a magnifying glass to examine fabrics. But whenever he could find time, he turned the lens upon more interesting things, among them insects, mites, and tadpoles.

The lens was of low power, yet it gave Leeuwenhoek glimpses of strange moving dots – living creatures, he thought – that were much smaller than the smallest insect. "If only I had a stronger lens!" he said. "If only I could examine these beasties!"

Eyes of Science

Leeuwenhoek's hobby led him to study the lens-grinder's craft. Soon he was grinding his own lenses, and learning to make them better and more powerful. To give high magnification, he found, a lens must be small, with a very great curvature. So he made smaller and smaller lenses, which looked almost like beads.

Perhaps Leeuwenhoek modelled his lenses after nature's own magnifier, the water drop. Do you know that a real microscope can be made by using a drop of water as a lens?

Cut a strip of metal from a tin can; then, using a thin nail, punch a hole in the centre of the strip. File down any jagged points around the hole, and work at it with a nail to make it quite round. Next, stick a needle in a piece of soft wood, as shown in the drawing. Attach the wood to the strip with a rubber band. The point of the needle should be opposite the hole. Place a nail between the wood and the metal strip. Then, using a pencil point, drip a small drop of water right into the hole.

Now you have a simple microscope, but a real one. It will magnify an object as much as a hundred times. Hold it up to the light, keeping the water drop quite close to your eye. By sliding the nail up and down, get the point of the needle into focus. It will look like a giant spike.

Leeuwenhoek's instrument was very much like this water-drop microscope. It was made of two metal plates riveted together, with the lens mounted between them. The specimen to be examined was held on a needle, or in a glass container, which could be moved into focus by turn-screws.

11

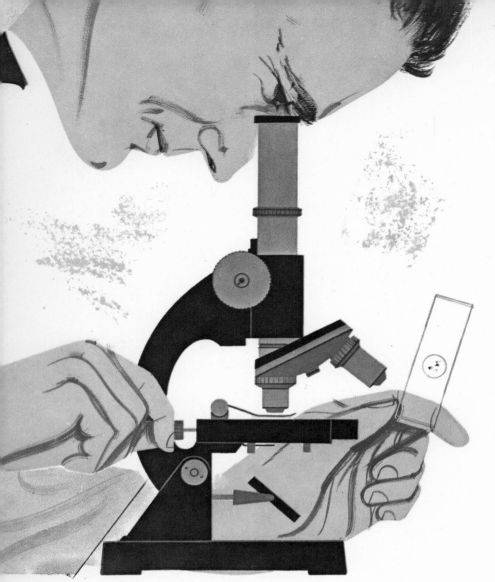

This modern microscope can magnify 1,000 times

A better kind of microscope was invented by mounting lenses in a tube—one at each end. This is how microscopes are made today. Instead of magnifying only one or two hundred times, they can magnify as much as one thousand times.

Using a Home-made Microscope

You can easily improve your water-drop microscope. Rest a pane of glass across two piles of books, as shown in the drawing. Take the metal strip with the hole in it, and bend it slightly near each end. Then, when it is laid on the glass, you can press with your fingers to move it up and down and get the proper focus.

Objects to be examined will be placed on the glass. But first arrange a small mirror under the glass, propping it up with an india rubber. Adjust the angle so that light from a window or a lamp is reflected up through the glass. It will shine right through the body of each creature you will examine.

12

A good place to hunt for specimens is a pool or pond with plants growing in it. If the water is greenish, so much the better. The green is the colour of microscopic plants.

Gather samples of water in small bottles. Take some water from the bottom. Scrape a bit of slime from the under side of a water-lily pad. Into another bottle, push some floating green scum, which is a mass of plants. By now, your bottles contain thousands of microscopic living things—micro-organisms. They make a garden and a zoo that you can investigate for weeks.

Micro-organisms can also be gathered from soil, and even from the air. Leeuwenhoek discovered this by setting out dishes of pure, fresh rain water and examining the water daily. Soon it was swarming with little creatures, which must have come from the air.

Such living specks are easily blown about. If a pool or puddle evaporates, the micro-organisms in it do not necessarily die. Each one has a chance of keeping alive. Perhaps it will shrink and form a crust around itself. Wind may lift the bit of life and carry it far away. If it falls into another moist place, it will soak up water and swell, then pop out of the crust and become active again.

This home-made microscope can magnify 100 times

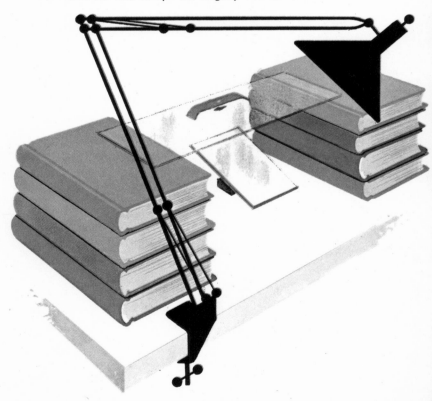

Because wind and water carry micro-organisms far and wide, the same kinds are found on every continent, and their marine relatives inhabit every sea.

World in a Water Drop

Multitudes of microscopic plants float in ponds, lakes, rivers, and the sea. Though single organisms are invisible, swarms of them often give the sea a greenish colour.

If we place a drop of sea water under a microscope, we may find it crowded with little plants. Many are globe-shaped; others are cylinders. A tough outer wall encloses and protects each one. The material inside is a sticky, jelly-like liquid. In it float little grains, which are green in some species, yellow in others, or a mixture of green, yellow, and blue-green. The green is chlorophyll. This and the other coloured substances enable the plant to absorb sunlight.

Among the microscopic plants are a great and numerous family called diatoms. Their name, meaning "cut in two", was given to them because of the way they look under the microscope. Each is enclosed in a shell divided into halves. One half fits over the edge of the other like the lid on an old-fashioned pill box. Diatoms build their shells of a substance dissolved in sea water. This is silica, the same substance that forms glass.

Tiny plants of another kind, called flagellates or "whip-bearers", are able to move by a peculiar sort of swimming. Examine a drop of water taken from a pond, and you are quite likely to find a whip-bearer of the group named Euglena. It is a trim, pretty thing, shaped like a spindle, with a thread curling from the front end. This is the "whip". It lashes to and fro, and pulls Euglena around in its water-drop world.

At Euglena's forward end there is a sort of groove, but it is not a mouth. Euglena has never been seen to swallow food. Like any green plant, it uses the power of sun-rays to make its own food. Beside the groove lies a red spot. This is probably sensitive to light, and helps to guide Euglena to well-lit water.

Microscopic plants and animals in a drop of water

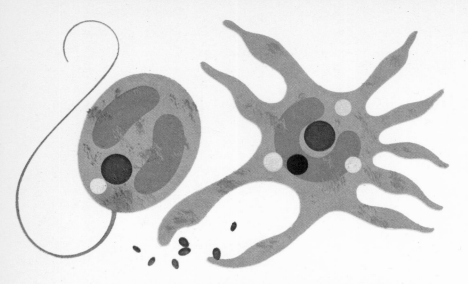

Microscopic Chrysamoeba, in two different forms

Are They Plants or Animals?

Certain whip-bearers—colourless ones—live by soaking up dissolved food substances. Even green Euglena, when kept in the dark, will lose its colour and stay alive by absorbing food if there is enough in the water.

A very remarkable whip-bearer is Chrysamoeba. It is green, and seems to live as a plant. But sometimes, after losing its whip, it behaves quite differently. Sticking to some surface, it crawls along by a sort of oozing. Part of its body substance bulges, forming an extension called a "false foot". More and more material flows into the false foot, and this drags the rest of the body forward.

When Chrysamoeba comes upon a particle of food, two or three false feet ooze toward the particle and close around it, enfolding it into the body. A strange creature, this Chrysamoeba! What are we to call it—plant or animal? It seems to be both!

Little and Lively

When Leeuwenhoek was examining drops of pond water, he came upon certain creatures with oval bodies. They were provided, he said, with many "thin little feet, or little legs, which were moved very nimbly, and which I was able to discover only after sundry great efforts, and wherewith they brought off incredibly quick motions."

This descriptions certainly fits members of the family called ciliates. Their name comes from the cilia—fine hairlike projections—that stick out all around the body. These are what Leeuwenhoek called "little legs". One very common ciliate, which

he must have seen often, is the slipper-shaped creature, Paramecium. Nothing could be livelier than this little animal. Its cilia flicker with a wavelike motion, which speeds the creature forward and, at the same time, makes it spin round and round.

The surface of Paramecium is folded in on one side, forming a groove. This leads backward to a tiny pore, which is the mouth of a funnel-like tube opening into the body. Cilia around the groove are constantly waving. Their motion stirs up a current, which brings in food particles such as bacteria.

These particles are taken into the body fluid with a bubble-shaped drop of water. As the drop floats around, chemicals seep into it and digest the food particles. We can watch them dissolve and disappear.

How the Great Are Like the Small

Creatures of the water-drop world appear quite unlike the plants and animals we see every day. But are they as different as we think? Let us see. Suppose we take a bit of leaf, sliced very thin, and put it under the microscope.

When magnified, the leaf seems to be divided into little chambers, each enclosed by its own wall. Three hundred years ago these objects were called

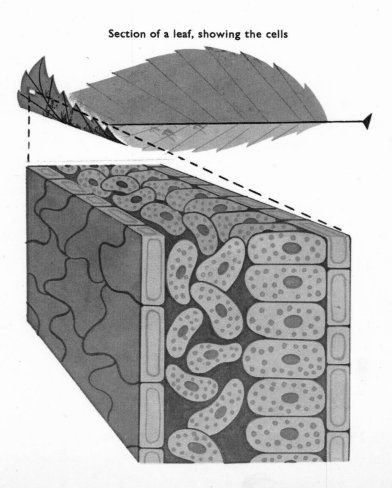

Section of a leaf, showing the cells

14

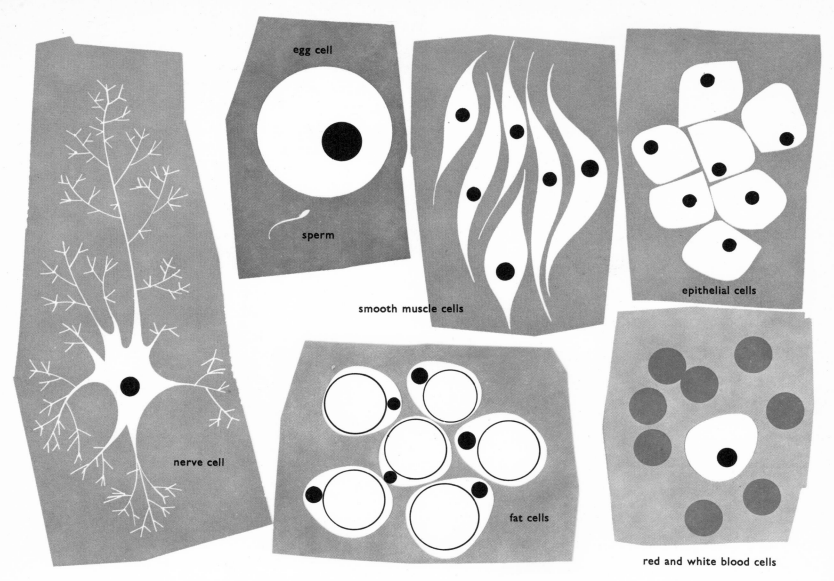

Cells which make up different tissues of the human body

cells, meaning little rooms. We still use this word, though we know that the most important thing about a cell is not its wall nor the space inside, but the material inside.

The substance of each cell is a clear, syrupy liquid. In it float many grains and bubble-shaped drops. Somewhere in the midst of the fluid is a globe-like object, the nucleus of the cell. It becomes very clear when the cell is treated with a stain, which colours the nucleus but not the rest of the fluid.

We also see a number of round or oval bodies, with smaller bodies inside them. In the smaller ones are flecks of green matter. This is chlorophyll, the stuff that makes leaves green. The cell fluid and its contents are surrounded by a delicate film—a membrane. Ordinarily this is hard to see because it lies close against the cell wall.

You are like a leaf in one way at least—your body

is made up of cells. So are all animal bodies. An animal cell lacks the chlorophyll and wall of a plant cell. But it has all the other things—the fluid, nucleus, and membrane. Clearly, plant and animal cells are built according to the same general plan.

Now, if we look again at creatures of the water-drop world, we recognise the parts found in cells. Each microscopic plant or animal has a similar fluid, a nucleus, and a membrane. Whether it be a whip-bearer, a ciliate, a diatom, or some other organism, it looks like a cell. And that is what it is—a single cell living by itself.

Thus, we see, a microscopic plant or animal is not completely different from a tree or an elephant. While these giants have billions of cells, and the micro-organism has only one, its single cell is the same type of unit that makes up the bodies of all the earth's creatures.

15

John Mayow's experiment: to find out what an animal takes from the air in breathing

Why Plants and Animals Need Air

You know that animals and people must breathe in order to stay alive. But why? Why is breathing necessary to keep them going?

This question fascinated a young English chemist, John Mayow, three hundred years ago. Hoping to find an answer, Mayow tried the following experiment. He set a mouse on a little stool, which was standing on the bottom of a tub containing a few inches of water. Over the mouse and stool he placed a jar, submerging the edges so that the mouse was shut off from the outside air. Then he set a lighted candle on another stool, and placed a jar over it in the same way.

As the candle burned, the level of the water under that jar rose slightly, but not up as far as the candle. In a little while the flame flickered out. Under the jar with the mouse, the water level also rose, but not up as far as the mouse. The mouse began gasping, and soon died.

This experiment proved that the burning candle took something from the air, and without that something the candle could not go on burning. The mouse also took something from the air, without which it could not live.

Did both the candle and the mouse use the same substance?

Mayow placed a lighted candle under the jar where the mouse had died. The flame went out at once. Then he enclosed a mouse and a lighted candle together under one jar. The candle went out. And the mouse, in Mayow's own words, "did not long survive its funeral torch. In fact, it continued breathing for little more than half the time it would have lived otherwise, without the candle."

16

Clearly, burning and breathing took the same substance from the air. What was this substance? Mayow never found out, and the question remained unanswered for a hundred years.

What is in the Air?

It happened that Joseph Priestley, an English minister from the manufacturing town of Leeds, lived beside a brewery. Fumes were always coming from the brewery, and Priestley, who was an amateur chemist, became curious about them. He visited the brewery, looked into the vats, and watched the gas bubbles popping from the malt. He held a burning splinter in the gas. The flame went out at once.

Priestley found the gas to be the same substance that is formed when candles burn and animals

The mouse in a jar of oxygen lived longer than the one in a jar of air

Joseph Priestley burning a candle in oxygen

breathe. Today we call it carbon dioxide. This is one of the gases found in air.

The minister-chemist also experimented with the gas later named oxygen, which makes up one fifth of the air. One day he filled a jar with oxygen and set a lighted candle inside. To his surprise, the candle flared up and burned very fast. When he placed a piece of glowing charcoal in the gas, it sparkled and burst into flame.

Priestley wondered if oxygen, which kept a flame burning so well, would be good for an animal to breathe. An experiment ought to tell. Priestley trapped some mice and placed two of them under bell jars – one with plain air and the other with pure oxygen. In fifteen minutes the mouse in plain air was dead. But the one in pure oxygen continued to breathe, and was still alive when Priestley removed it after half an hour.

From this he concluded that oxygen was perfectly good to breathe – in fact, it seemed better than plain air.

17

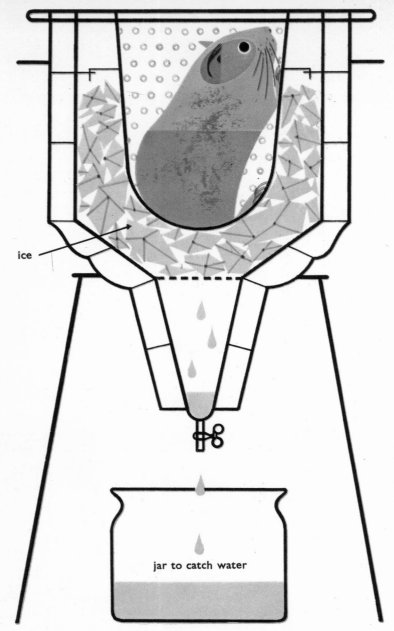

ice

jar to catch water

Device used by Lavoisier to measure the heat produced
by an animal

charcoal in the vessel, feeding the flame with oxygen, which he measured carefully. He also measured the amount of ice melted by the heat. Then he put the guinea pig in the vessel and measured the same two things – the oxygen used and the heat produced.

In ten hours, the guinea pig used the same amount of oxygen as the ounce of burning charcoal. And its body heat melted the same amount of ice. This showed that the guinea pig produced about as much heat as the ounce of charcoal.

Now Lavoisier could say: "Respiration is truly a form of combustion. Though a slower process, it is perfectly similar to the burning of a fuel. Thus the air we breathe supports the inner flame of life that keeps us warm."

The Great Work of Plants

Breathing and burning go on all the time all over the world, so oxygen is always being used up. And yet, after millions of years, there is still a vast amount of it in the air. Clearly, new oxygen must be added to take the place of what is used up. Where does it come from?

Scientists found the answer when they discovered that green plants, in daylight, give off oxygen. We can thank the world's plants for keeping the air supplied with the precious gas we breathe.

Not only that, but plants purify the air by taking carbon dioxide from it.

What do plants do with carbon dioxide? A scientist of Switzerland, Nicolas de Saussure, found the answer. He knew, as you probably do, that carbon

Breathing and Burning

Oxygen was given its name by the great French chemist, Antoine Lavoisier. He had heard of Priestley's experiments, and thought they showed some close connection between breathing and burning.

He reasoned: the burning of a fuel uses up oxygen and produces carbon dioxide, and so does the breathing of an animal. Burning fuel gives off heat, and so does a breathing animal. Does this mean that breathing is some kind of burning?

Lavoisier tested this idea with a guinea pig. The apparatus for his experiment was a double-walled vessel which could hold chopped ice between its outer and inner walls.

As his first step, Lavoisier burned an ounce of

18

Antoine Lavoisier, the great French chemist

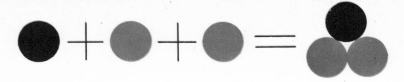

Carbon + oxygen + oxygen = carbon dioxide
$C + O + O = CO_2$

dioxide is a combination of carbon and oxygen. A common form of carbon is charcoal. Carbon is a chemical element – one of the hundred or more substances that cannot be broken down into other substances. Oxygen also is an element.

Each element has its own particular kind of atom. If two or more different kinds of atoms combine, they form a compound. Carbon dioxide is a compound; its smallest particle – its molecule – is made of two oxygen atoms linked to one carbon atom.

Wood can be turned into charcoal because it is rich in carbon. So is bread – which you prove when you burn a slice of toast. The black is carbon. All plant substances are rich in carbon, and this brings up the question, "Does plant carbon come from carbon dioxide of the air?"

Saussure thought so, and tried to prove it. He set a plant under a jar, along with a substance that removed carbon dioxide from the air. The plant stopped growing. After three weeks, its leaves died and fell.

Other plants were kept in air having the usual amount of carbon dioxide. They grew normally. Some were kept in air to which several times the usual amount of carbon dioxide was added. They grew faster than normal.

Then Saussure charred the several plants and weighed their carbon. There was more in the plants that had the better supply of carbon dioxide.

This experiment showed that plants get their carbon from the carbon dioxide of the air.

Gift from the Air

The percentage of carbon dioxide in the air is small – only three parts in ten thousand. But this is enough to supply forests, grasses, field crops, and all plants of the land. Carbon dioxide dissolves in water, so there is plenty in the sea for plants to use.

Both on land and in the sea, plants are always using carbon dioxide to grow and build their substance. Scientists have made this estimate: In one year, the world's plants take 150,000 million tons of carbon from the air and lock it into plant material.

This means that in a few years plants use up an amount of carbon dioxide equal to the whole content in the atmosphere. Yet the supply never gives out. That is because new carbon dioxide is always being added to the air. Some comes from the decay of dead plants and animals, and some from the breathing of animals and people.

So the air is kept supplied with carbon dioxide, just as it is kept supplied with oxygen. Each gas is always circulating between the air and living things. The supply of each gas stays about the same, so there is always enough for the earth's creatures.

On land and in water, animals breathe in oxygen (O) and breathe out carbon dioxide (CO_2)

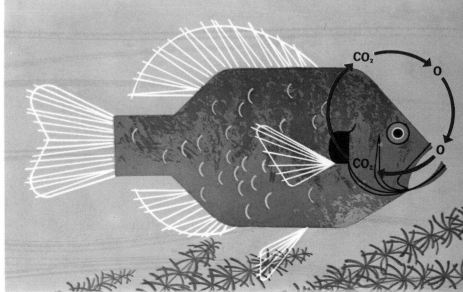

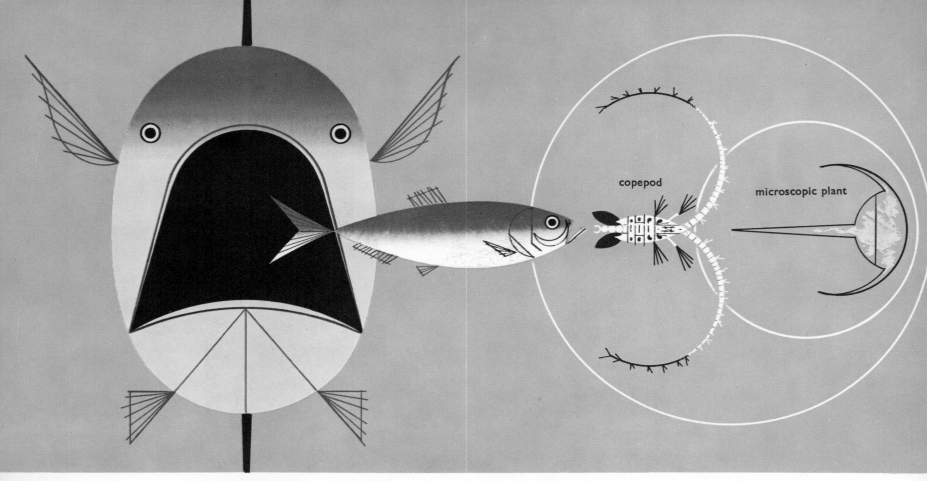

Food Chain in the Sea. The big fish eats the small fish that eats the copepod that eats the microscopic plant

The Marvellous Story of Food

No matter what you eat, you can thank plants for it. Some of your food—cereals, fruit, vegetables – comes straight from plants. Some of it—eggs, meat, dairy products – comes from animals. But the chickens that lay the eggs, and the cattle that give the meat and milk, are eaters of plant food. As the saying goes, "All flesh is grass." All your food, if you trace it back far enough, comes from plants.

In the sea, as on land, food is made by plants, and only by plants. A tuna eats smaller fishes, these eat little animals, and the little animals eat microscopic plants. Everywhere, the chain of food leads back to plants. They alone make the food that nourishes us and all the world's animals.

Food and Energy

When you work or play hard, you use up energy. This makes you hungry. You eat, and then you can work or play again, because you get new energy from your food.

Just how is energy obtained from food?

Antoine Lavoisier thought this was like asking: How is heat produced from fuel? His answer to the second question was simple. Burning, he said, is the joining of the fuel substance with oxygen from the air. Fuels like coal, oil, and wood are rich in carbon. When they burn, their carbon unites with oxygen to form carbon dioxide. In chemical language, the carbon is oxidized.

Breathing, like burning, uses up oxygen and produces carbon dioxide. The carbon in this gas, Lavoisier reasoned, must come from food. He said, "We and other creatures obtain energy from the slow burning of food."

To test this idea, he performed several experiments. This time his subject was not a guinea pig, but a friend and fellow scientist, Armand Séguin.

Séguin breathed oxygen through a tube, and Lavoisier carefully measured the amount he used. First Séguin fasted; then he ate. Sometimes he rested; sometimes he worked. Lavoisier found that

20

his subject used more oxygen after eating than when fasting, and more while at work than when resting. This proved that a person gets his energy from the burning, or oxidation, of food.

The Explosive Gas in Food and Water

Besides carbon, another important element in food is hydrogen. When it is by itself, hydrogen is a gas. It is colourless and odourless, and much lighter than air. Because of its lightness, hydrogen was formerly used to fill balloons and airships, but this had to be stopped because the gas often caught fire and exploded.

About two hundred years ago, scientists began to make some surprising discoveries about hydrogen. One man mixed a small amount with air and burned the mixture in a flask. Afterwards he found droplets of water, like dew, on the inside of the flask.

A great English chemist, Henry Cavendish, thought this dew must be formed by the combining of the hydrogen with some gas in the air. What gas? Suspecting it was oxygen, Cavendish tried to burn hydrogen mixed with oxygen. He did this many times, with the two gases mixed in various proportions. Each time, he noticed that some of the gas mixture disappeared.

Finally, Cavendish mixed two parts of hydrogen with one of oxygen, and lighted the mixture. There was a powerful explosion. Both gases vanished completely, leaving only water in their place. The water weighed exactly as much as the gases that had formed it – nothing was lost.

This experiment showed precisely what water is made of – two parts of hydrogen to one part of oxygen. As the chemist explains it, the water molecule is built of two atoms of hydrogen linked with one of oxygen.

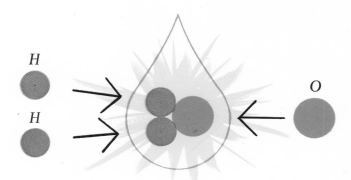

Hydrogen + hydrogen + oxygen = water
H + H + O = H₂O

Just as the burning of hydrogen forms water vapour, so does the burning of coal, oil, petrol, or wax. Light a candle and lower an open glass jar over the flame for a few seconds. The inside of the jar becomes "steamed up" with tiny water droplets. The same thing happens if a perfectly dry crust of bread is burned instead of a candle. Why? The answer, of course, is that foods and fuels contain hydrogen. In burning, the hydrogen unites with oxygen to form water vapour.

Lavoisier measuring the amount of oxygen a man uses

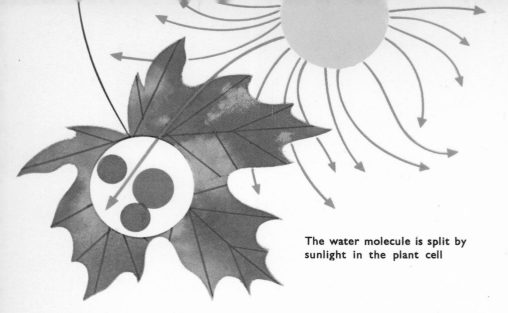

The water molecule is split by sunlight in the plant cell

How Plants Store Energy

Coal and oil are formed of plant material, and food is a plant product. So we know that plants do the work of putting hydrogen into food and fuels. But where do they get the hydrogen?

In 1941 a team of American chemists tested the oxygen given off by plants and found that it comes from water. This means that plants somehow break up water into the gases that form it—hydrogen and oxygen. The hydrogen goes into the making of plant products.

How is the hydrogen separated from the oxygen? This takes energy, and the energy is provided by sunlight. Caught by grains of chlorophyll in the plant cell, sunlight splits water molecules into hydrogen and oxygen. Most of the oxygen passes from the cell and out of the plant.

What happens to the hydrogen? Atoms of hydrogen remain dissolved in the cell fluid. They are held by molecules of a substance called an enzyme, which acts as a chemical helper. Carbon dioxide molecules also are dissolved in the fluid. The enzymes join the hydrogen atoms to the carbon dioxide. The joining goes on until a molecule is built with the following atoms: 6 of carbon, 12 of hydrogen, and 6 of oxygen. The chemist writes this: $C_6H_{12}O_6$. This molecule is a simple kind of sugar. So you see, sugar is just carbon dioxide holding on to hydrogen. When sugar is burned as food, the hydrogen is taken out again, leaving the carbon dioxide.

The sunlight energy used in the splitting of water is not lost. It is packed into food in the form of chemical energy. When a food molecule is burned, there is something like a small-scale explosion of hydrogen and oxygen—an explosion without a bang. The joining of the hydrogen and oxygen atoms releases some of the stored energy of the food. This energy, which comes from sunlight, keeps plants alive. And since animals and people eat plants, it keeps them alive, too.

Green Factories

In the simple sugar molecule, the carbon atoms are linked in a chain, with the hydrogen and oxygen atoms attached. This chain is a lively thing. It curves into a loop, unloops, and loops again. Its ends wriggle around. With the help of an enzyme molecule, the chain hooks on to another like itself. In combining, the two chains form a double sugar molecule. One such molecule is the kind of sugar you buy in the store.

A simple sugar molecule made by a plant

The linking process goes further. It works like a factory assembly line. Many simple molecules are joined to form a big, complicated molecule. Still the linking goes on. Big molecules are finally built into a solid grain floating in the cell fluid. This is starch, which can be kept in storage until it is needed. Sugars and starches are called carbohydrates. This means that their molecule is made of carbon, plus hydrogen and oxygen in a 2 to 1 ratio, as in water.

There are two other "assembly lines" in the cell. On one of these, the final product is fat. A fat has the same three kinds of atoms as a carbohydrate, but they are linked in a different sort of chain.

On the third assembly line, the final product is protein. A protein also is a carbon chain with hydrogen and oxygen attached. In addition, another kind of atom is linked on—nitrogen.

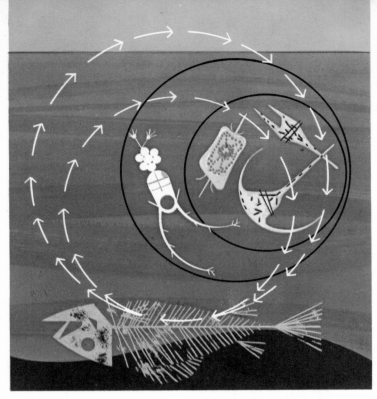

In the sea, nitrogen from dead bodies is used by plants

The Nitrogen Story

Nitrogen exists as a gas in the atmosphere. In fact, four out of every five air molecules are nitrogen. Billions of tons of the gas surround the earth, but in its pure form nitrogen is useless to plants. It is a lazy element, which does not unite readily with others to form usable compounds.

Only a few living things are able to make something useful of nitrogen. Among them are bacteria found in the soil and the sea. These micro-organisms take pure nitrogen from the air and link it into compounds called nitrates, which plants can use.

Nitrates dissolved in water seep into a plant and enter every cell. With the help of enzymes, they start on the protein assembly line. First they link into molecules called amino acids. Then these join to make proteins. Some proteins are built of hundreds, even thousands, of amino acid links.

When plants are eaten by animals, the proteins go into the making of animal flesh and blood. All over the world, plants are always taking usable nitrates from the soil and the sea, and animals are eating plants. As a result, most of the world's nitrate supply has become locked up in living things.

How long can this go on? Will there come a day when all creatures will be starved for nitrogen?

There is no such danger, for the soil and the sea always get the nitrogen back. When plants and animals die, their bodies decay. Bacteria work upon them and change their proteins back to simpler compounds. In this way, usable nitrogen is returned to the soil and the sea. Then plants absorb and use it again.

So the great cycle of life goes on. The sun shines, and plants make food. The food nourishes the plants themselves, and also gives animals their body-building materials and energy. This energy, which came from the sun, keeps the flame of life burning in every plant and animal on earth.

On land, soil bacteria make nitrates from nitrogen of the air. The nitrates are used by plants that are eaten by animals. When plants and animals die, the nitrogen goes back to the soil and the air

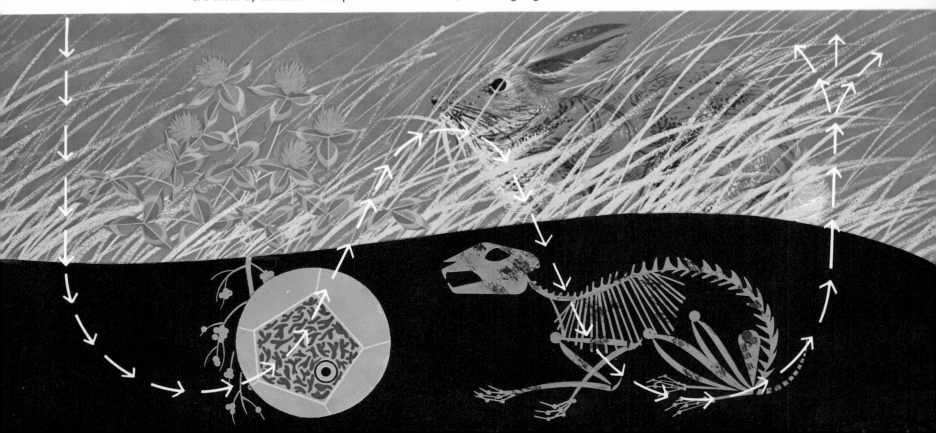

The Web of Life

The earth has many kinds of homes for living things. It has sea and land; it has desert, forest, and grassland. Each home seems just right for the plants and animals living there. The place is right, and so are the neighbours. The various inhabitants provide food, shelter, and other things for one another. All are connected by their needs – all are held together in one great web of life.

Dwellers of the Desert

In the south-western part of North America, winds and mountain ranges work together to make deserts. The winds blow from the west. They carry moisture from the Pacific Ocean, but cannot carry much of it over the long, high mountains in their path. The winds become chilled while rising over the ranges, and this causes their moisture to fall as snow and rain. After they have passed the mountains, the winds have little rain left for the land.

In other regions, there are always enough water droplets in the air to stop some of the sun's rays. And moisture evaporating from plants, bodies of water, and damp soil brings a merciful coolness. But in the desert, glaring sunlight bakes the ground.

After months or years of drought there may be a brief downpour, but most of the water quickly runs off and evaporates. A desert plant must be equipped to benefit from rain that comes seldom and briefly. It has wide-spreading roots, which quickly suck up a good deal of water. This may be the only moisture the plant will receive for a year, or for several years.

Some kinds of desert plants live only after the rains. Springing up from seeds, they flower, drop their own seeds, and then die. Months or years later, if rain comes, the seeds sprout, and a new generation of plants flourishes for a brief while.

All plants give off moisture through their leaves and other green surfaces. The more green surface there is, the greater the loss of water. A large oak may lose barrels of water a day. This would not do in the desert, where a plant must save water.

Cacti are great water-savers. Their surface is small, so they lose very little water by evaporation.

The barrel cactus is just one thick stem, shaped more or less like a barrel. Outside, it is dry as dust, but the "barrel" contains a juicy pulp that may hold gallons of water. Sharp spines stick out around the cactus, guarding it against thirsty animals.

Desert animals get water mainly from juices in their food. Many creatures manage to live without any other source of moisture. Desert rats, mice, and ground squirrels feed on seeds that are quite dry. When this food (or any other) is burned in an animal's body, it yields a little water. This is enough for a desert mouse or rat.

Animals are often active in the daytime, and become heated from their exertions. Some get rid of excess heat by sweating, others by panting, Evaporation of sweat, or of moisture from the lining of mouth and lungs, helps to cool an animal. Where water is plentiful, it hardly matters how much moisture he loses – he can always get more simply by taking a drink.

In the desert, where little or no water is to be found, body fluid cannot be wasted for cooling. So a desert animal avoids sweating and panting in the sun. Instead, he hides under the ground in a cool burrow.

Rats and other rodents dig their own burrows. So do a number of lizards. Snakes make themselves at home in shelters built by the rodents. Even a bird, the burrowing owl, takes refuge in the earth. It lives, nests, and raises its young in rodents' burrows. What would the birds and reptiles do without the rodents?

While the sun glares, the desert is empty, dead. But as soon as night falls, small shadowy things creep like ghosts from the earth. Rodents scurry about looking for seeds. Large lizards trail small ones. Owls and snakes hunt the very rodents that built their underground homes.

In such ways, the desert community lives. Some of its animals feed on the seeds and fruits of plants; others prey upon the plant-eaters. None could live without the real pioneers and conquerors of the desert – its plants.

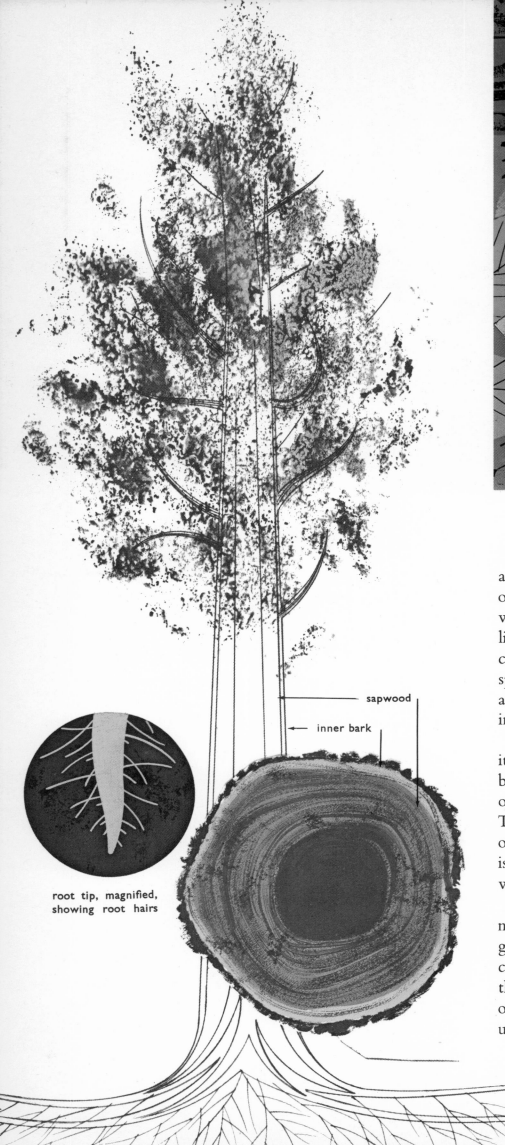

sapwood

inner bark

root tip, magnified,
showing root hairs

The Workings of a Tree

Forests need a wet climate, for trees use vast amounts of water. A tree's roots go deep, and branch out widely in all directions, so they soak up a lot of water. The tips of the roots are covered with millions of microscopic root hairs, which greatly increase their surface. If all the root hairs could be split and spread out flat, they would cover several acres. Through this enormous surface, the tree drinks in moisture from the soil.

Water passes from the roots to the trunk. There it rises in the sapwood, which lies beneath the inner bark. The trunk may be very tall. A giant redwood or sequoia sometimes grows more than 300 feet tall. This is about the height of a thirty-story building. In order to send water to the top of a skyscraper, a pump is needed. How does a tree, without a pump, raise water 300 feet or more?

This is part of its secret: the water tubes are very narrow, and there are thousands of them. All together, they have a lot of inside surface which water can wet. Water molecules have forces that make them a little sticky. They stick to surfaces, and to one another. So they wet the wall of a tube and creep upward, pulling one another in a long, fine thread.

The streamlets carry dissolved materials of two kinds. One is a group of atoms that come from the minerals in soil. The other is nitrogen in the form of usable compounds.

The water that carries these things is itself a building material. In the leaves, water molecules are split by sunlight, and their hydrogen links with carbon dioxide to form sugar. The carbon dioxide is taken in through little openings in the leaves.

Some sugar molecules are burned for energy. Others become linked into long chains to form molecules of cellulose. This is the building material of cell walls and wood.

Sugar is needed for energy and construction in all living parts of the tree. It is carried in watery sap, which passes from leaves to branches to trunk. The sap goes down the trunk through tubes in the inner bark. It reaches the very roots, to nourish their cells.

For all this activity, the tree needs a vast supply of water. It takes a thousand pounds of water to make one pound of wood. Only a small part of all this water is used for its hydrogen. The rest evaporates from the leaves. It goes out through the same little openings that take in carbon dioxide. In fact, carbon dioxide is caught from the air because the openings are wet, and the gas dissolves in the moisture.

Evaporation from the leaves is necessary to keep the water streamlets flowing upward. As water is lost from tubes at the top of the system, a force is created which pulls upon the water in lower sections of the tubes. The water threads are drawn up and up, and reach the leaves at the very top of the tree.

The Forest Community

The forest produces millions of tons of leaves, branches, roots, and trunks. If all this living matter kept on increasing without check, the stores of nitrogen and minerals in the soil would be used up, and the trees would all starve. But several things happen to prevent this.

Dead leaves and branches fall, piling up on the ground to form a bed of litter. Trees themselves age and die and crash to the ground. All this woody litter becomes food for hosts of creatures. Termites and carpenter-ants bore through it; so do the wormlike grubs of many beetles. Tough fungus plants, relatives of the mushrooms, spring from fallen trunks and branches. Before the outside part of a fungus appears, its pale threads have spread through the wood.

Fuzzlike moulds cover and creep into bits of crumbling litter. These are plants that lack chlorophyll, so they cannot make their own food. Instead, they settle on dead litter, and ooze a juice containing digestive enzymes. The enzymes break down cellulose into sugar, which is soaked up as food.

Under the litter is a bed of dark, moist, spongy earth. This is mostly humus, half-rotted material left from plants. In it, invisible bacteria are at work. They, too, dissolve and digest woody remains.

Insects, fungus plants, and bacteria, working in their various ways, help to break down the dead matter of the forest, and change it back to simple materials that the trees can use again. And so, through death and decay, the forest lives.

In the shelter of the forest, hosts of animals find protection and food. Birds eat insects that feed on leaves. Squirrels, mice, and rats eat nuts and seeds. Deer browse on saplings. Owls, skunks, and weasels hunt the smaller plant-eaters. Members of the cat and dog families hunt the larger plant-eaters. Bears and raccoons gather plant food, and also catch animals.

Altogether, the forest harbours a great community. Its members dwell in their own nooks and on their own levels, from the high leafy crowns to the littered ground. But all — the fungus plants, the bacteria, the birds, the plant-eaters, the flesh-eaters — all depend on the trees. The trees create the food from which the whole community lives.

The Grasslands

In the eastern part of North America, early settlers from Europe found the land covered with forest. It took some work to cut and burn away trees, but once a patch of ground had been cleared, ploughing it was easy, for the soil was soft and almost bare of plants.

By 1840, most of the eastern woodland had been settled, and pioneers were moving westward in search of new land. After they had passed beyond the Mississippi, they came to a border line where the forest ended. On one side of the border were trees; on the other side was grass. The pioneers came to a halt. They gazed with awe upon a land like an endless sea—but a sea of tall, waving grass.

For many years, the pioneers struggled with the prairie. No matter how hard they tried, they could not plough that rich soil. The roots of the tall grass were deep and tangled, making a densely matted sod. To drag a plough through it, as many as six yoke of oxen were needed. And they did not have enough animals to break the ground.

Prairie soil is deep and dark, for black humus is mixed all through it. The humus comes largely from the decay of dead roots, which often go down several feet. Because the deep soil is cool, the humus there decays slowly. Nitrogen and other nutrients are supplied from it steadily, and rainfall is not great enough to wash them away.

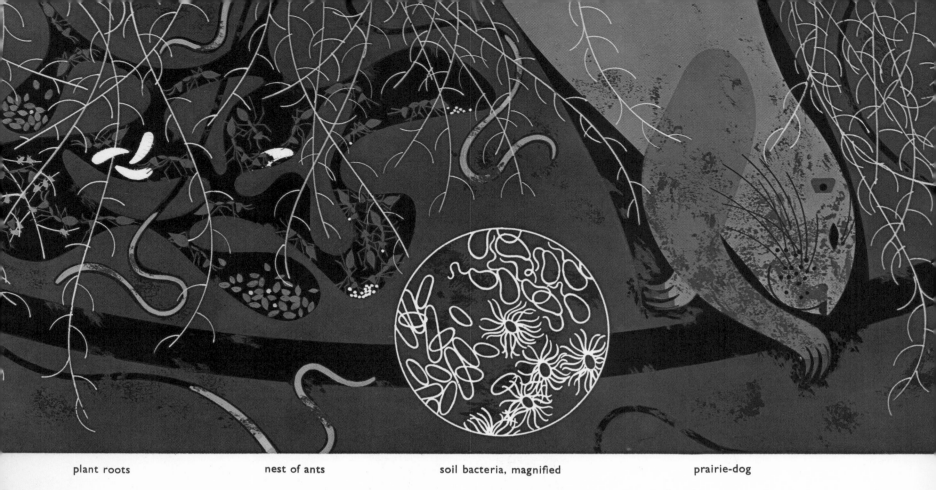

plant roots   nest of ants   soil bacteria, magnified   prairie-dog

How different prairie soil is from forest soil! In woodland, a very large part of the nutrient supply is locked up in living trees, or is washed away by rains. In grassland, much more remains in the soil, ready for use.

Humus in the soil acts as a sponge, soaking up rain-water. It also helps to hold together particles of clay and sand, binding them into loose crumbs of various sizes. Plant roots creep between the crumbs and into them. They penetrate a million tiny pores, where root hairs touch the grains of soil and suck up moisture that clings to their surfaces.

Grassland soil makes a home for multitudes of creatures. Earthworms busily tunnel through it, feeding as they go. Ants build underground cities. Various kinds of grubs feed upon roots, and centi-pedes feed upon the grubs. Moles and shrews hunt worms. Mice gather seeds. Prairie-dogs burrow and build.

All these restless creatures, large and small, help to mix the soil and open passages through which air and water can enter. The greatest work of all is done by vast unseen armies of bacteria. In a handful of soil there may be a hundred million. Some kinds of soil bacteria capture nitrogen from the air; others recover it from dead plant and animal matter.

Long before the coming of white men, and even before the Indians came, the grasslands supported herds of camels, elephants, rhinos, antelopes, horses. Until quite recently, they were still the home of bison and antelope, which were hunted by wolves and pumas.

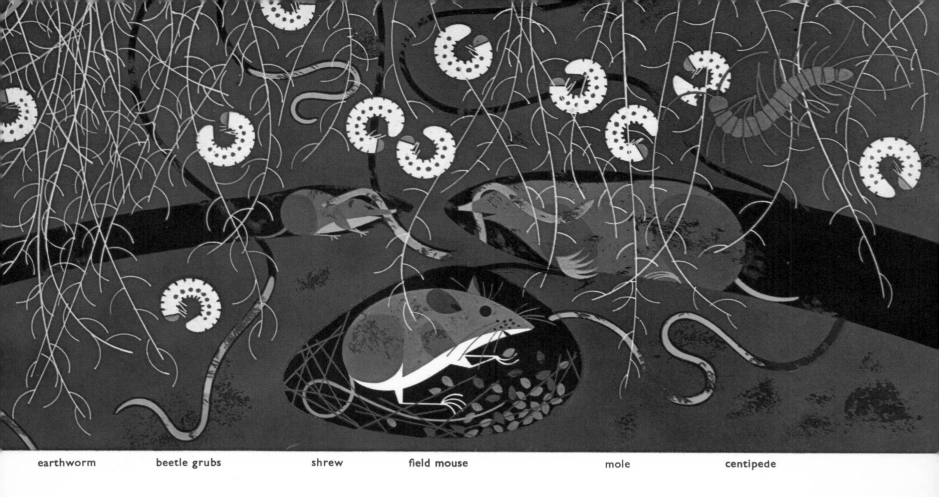

earthworm   beetle grubs   shrew   field mouse   mole   centipede

Down through the centuries an unending struggle raged along the border between forest and grassland. The struggle was between trees and grass. The seeds of trees blew into the prairie, and seeds of grass blew into the woodland. Both kinds of invading seeds would sprout on foreign soil, but then the seedlings died. On the prairie, grasses choked out the tree seedlings. In the forest, trees shaded out the grass. Where either kind of plant was well established, it was hard for the other to invade.

In the battle, fire fought on the side of grass. Often, a fire started by lightning would burn down a stretch of forest along the border. Before new trees could grow up, grasses seeded and occupied the ground. Fire was harmless to grass – even helpful. Where grass above ground had been burned away,

the roots sent up a new growth, thicker than the old.

The Indians often lit fires as a means of driving game. And so, because of man-made and natural fires, grasses spread at the expense of forest.

Today, where trees have been protected from fire, the forest has won back some lost ground. At this very moment, around stretches of the Canadian prairie, trees are advancing into the grassland.

But greater things than this have happened since the prairie was settled. Cattle have replaced the bison and antelope. And the soil that used to support wild grasses now supports wheat and corn. These grain plants are really grasses tamed and improved by man, so they thrive in the grassland soil. And from this new wealth of the prairie, millions of people make their living.

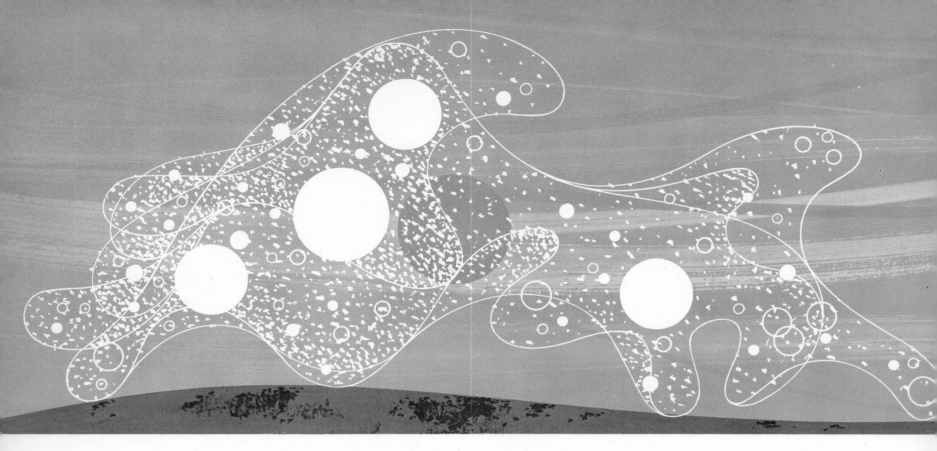

Amoeba, a microscopic pond animal, moving along a leaf

Fluid that Lives

You have looked at living things from several different points of view, as a biologist does. But do you really know what keeps a plant or animal alive? The best way to understand this is to look right into the fluid of a living cell, and see it at work.

A large, active cell is easy to watch, so let us begin with a certain one-celled animal that lives in ponds. Its name is *Amoeba proteus*, which means "Amoeba of the changing form."

The Animal with False Feet

Under the microscope, Amoeba looks like a blob of soft, colourless jelly. This stuff is its cell fluid – its protoplasm. Like every cell, Amoeba has a filmy membrane around it. The membrane is sticky, which helps the little animal to cling to surfaces. It sticks to a leaf, for example, and moves along in a peculiar way. Somewhere in the blob, the fluid begins to ooze outward, making a bulge. Such a bulge is called a false foot. Only the tip of it touches the leaf.

After a while another false foot bulges out near the first one, in a slightly different direction. As the fluid oozes, it makes Amoeba roll along on its false feet like a tractor rolling over its track. Meanwhile, the back end bunches into knoblike shapes. There the membrane seems to be shrinking and squeezing the fluid forward.

Protoplasm

What sort of fluid is this, that can behave in such lively fashion? To begin with, protoplasm is about nine-tenths water. Scattered through the water are several kinds of long chain molecules. Of these, the proteins are the most important. They easily join together, forming strands. The strands do not settle nor collect in a mass. They stay scattered throughout the water. As a scientist would say, they are suspended in it.

Very small particles of many substances will act in this way in water. The water itself helps to keep them suspended. Water molecules are always in motion, flitting around like a swarm of gnats. They bounce particles this way and that, and the bouncing holds them up. This kind of system is known as a colloidal solution.

In protoplasm, there is a special arrangement that helps to keep strands of protein from collecting in a mass. The proteins are "water-loving". This means that each attracts water molecules and holds them in a film around its surface. So if proteins join, they join loosely, forming an open network.

You can do a little experiment with gelatin, which is a protein, to see how protein molecules behave in water. Mix some powdered gelatin in hot water and you have a liquid that flows easily. But chill it, and you see a striking change. The solution congeals.

Forces of attraction in the protein molecules have caused them to link and form strands. The strands lace together in an invisible network. Water is trapped in pockets in the network, so it cannot flow. As you say, the gelatin has set. As the chemist says, it has changed from the sol or liquid state and become a gel.

The gel can easily be liquefied. Warm it slightly, or beat or shake it. This separates the protein strands. The network comes apart, and the water can flow again. But let the liquid stand, and it turns back to gel.

All this helps to explain the behaviour of an Amoeba. The creature moves by a constant shifting of its protoplasm back and forth between the sol and gel states. Just under the membrane, a layer of protoplasm will gel. In doing so, it squeezes the liquid protoplasm inside, making it ooze.

A Cell at Work

When Amoeba's protoplasm streams outward, what keeps it from leaking into the water? By using a fine glass needle as a tool, it is possible to cut an Amoeba right in two. Liquid protoplasm touches the water, but doesn't leak away. The surface of the protoplasm immediately gels, forming a membrane. In the same way, a membrane develops around a streaming false foot. Why?

The forming of a membrane is helped by a substance dissolved in the water where Amoebas live.

This is calcium, which comes from soil and rock. A little calcium tends to make protoplasm become a gel, but too much will cause it to stiffen so it cannot liquefy again.

We can prove this with an Amoeba under the microscope. First we add extra calcium to the water. Then we cut the Amoeba, allowing the calcium to seep into it. Soon the protoplasm turns stiff and motionless. The Amoeba is dead.

There are other substances in water which act to keep protoplasm liquid. One of these is potassium. If we add potassium to the water and then cut the Amoeba, its cell fluid streams out and mixes with the water. It keeps escaping until none is left, and there is no Amoeba.

Such accidents are not likely to happen to an Amoeba in its natural home. Pond water has a good balance of calcium and potassium. The pond is just right for the Amoeba, and the Amoeba is suited to the pond.

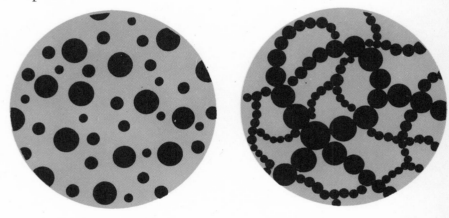

Sol: particles scattered   Gel: particles in a network

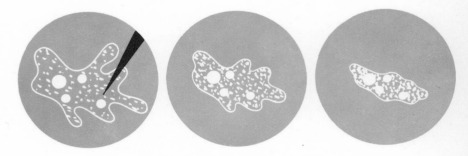

Torn Amoeba. Above: in water with too much calcium
Below: in water with too much potassium

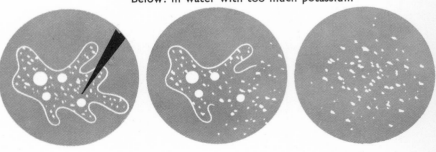

It Multiplies by Dividing

While oozing along a leaf or stem, Amoeba will come upon a bit of food – perhaps a tiny whip-bearer. Extending false feet over and around the creature, Amoeba holds it down and finally engulfs it. The luckless whip-bearer floats around inside the Amoeba in a droplet of water. It struggles for a while, then starts to dissolve. It is being digested.

A well-fed Amoeba grows for several hours, or for a day, but it can't grow beyond a certain size. If it did, its surface would get smaller and smaller in relation to the amount of material inside. The Amoeba receives all its oxygen through the membrane, and gets rid of waste matter through it, too. For proper functioning, the Amoeba must remain small. Then it has a relatively large surface through which materials can pass.

As if to solve the problem of size, a full-grown Amoeba does a remarkable thing. It splits into two smaller copies of itself. The process of division takes less than an hour. When it is about to begin, the Amoeba pulls in its false feet and becomes round. Things are happening in the middle of it. Thread-like particles have gathered in the nucleus. The membrane of the nucleus dissolves, and the particles line up across the cell. Each particle splits length-wise. This makes two sets, which move apart. Each set becomes enclosed in a membrane, forming a separate nucleus. Then Amoeba pinches together in the middle. The halves separate, and behold, each is a new Amoeba!

50,000 Billion Cells in You

Every large organism is made of multitudes of cells. Your own body has fifty thousand billion or more. Each is a tiny blob of protoplasm enclosed in a membrane. There are different kinds of cells, forming different tissues, such as skin, muscle, and bone.

In most of your tissues, cells are closely packed, yet a watery fluid can seep into and between them. Each cell lives in this fluid just as a microscopic organism lives in the water of pond or sea. The fluid contains dissolved oxygen and food substances, which trickle into the cell through its membrane. Carbon dioxide and other waste materials trickle out.

As a cell is nourished, it builds up protoplasm and grows. But it must not grow too large, for then the membrane would be too small to let in enough food and oxygen. So the cell, like an Amoeba, splits into two new cells. These replace cells that die.

In most tissues of your body, cells divide and reproduce as long as you live. Just a few kinds of cells —your nerve cells, for example—stopped dividing before you were born. They have been growing but not multiplying, so you have the same nerve cells all your life.

Amoeba feeding: it engulfs a smaller animal

Amoeba dividing into two

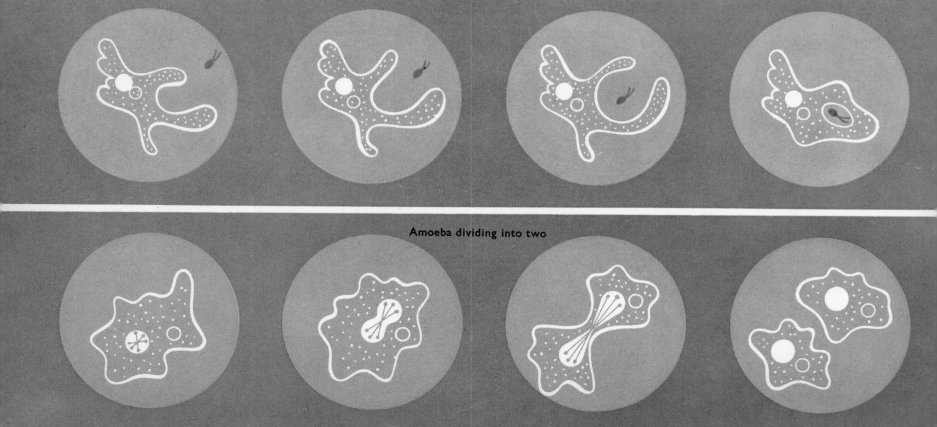

Why Cells Can Move and Work

When you bend your arm, your muscle does the work—but how?

Muscle is made of long protein fibres wrapped in a bundle. Each end of the bundle is attached to a bone. The fibres shorten and pull on the bones, and this moves your arm.

Everything depends on the fact that the fibres have the power to shorten—to contract. They are able to do this because they are made of protein threads with ends fitting together. When a certain chemical acts upon them, the threads slip past one another, making the whole fibre shorten.

Often, protoplasm contracts and relaxes in rhythm, like a pulse. This is easy to observe in the slime mould, a simple organism that lives in decaying woody material.

Muscle fibres, enlarged

Muscle in action

In one way, the slime mould resembles a plant. It produces tiny spores, from which new organisms grow. These organisms are microscopic things that look and act like Amoebas. They creep around on moist surfaces inside heaps of rotting wood or leaves. A number will meet and merge to form a single mass of protoplasm. This can go on until there is a sheet of clear slime an inch or several inches across.

Under the microscope, a slime mould looks like a lump of gel with tunnels containing fluid protoplasm. The gel contracts, squeezing the fluid and causing it to stream through the tunnels. The streaming goes one way, pauses, then goes backward, and the whole movement continues to ebb and flow.

The slime mould imitates the pumping action of your own heart. In the heart, muscle fibres contract, making the walls press in and squeeze blood into the arteries. The slime mould pulses, and your heart beats, because the power to contract is built into their protein fibres.

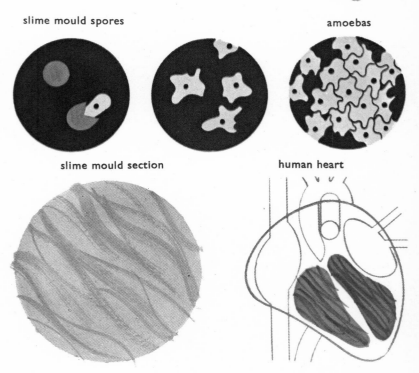

slime mould spores

amoebas

slime mould section

human heart

The network structure of protoplasm is also help-ful in other ways. Because it is usually loose, water can stream through it freely. Small molecules carried in the water reach and act upon larger molecules. Very often, no doubt, molecules collide without having any effect on one another. But all is not confusion. Protoplasm has a traffic system, which the streaming molecules obey.

Raw material molecules flow to their proper as-sembly lines, and there combine into sugar, fat, and protein. The sugar and fat serve as stores of chemical energy. The protein is built into structures of the cell.

When energy is needed, the proper enzymes go to work. Step by step, food molecules are taken apart. Hydrogen atoms are detached, to unite with oxygen and form water. This is burning, or oxidation. On it goes, unlocking energy from the molecules.

It would be awkward to have all the cell's energy stored in big units—like money in thousand pound notes. Small coins are needed in daily life; small packets of energy are needed in the cell. The small coins of the cell are molecules of a substance known as ATP, which stands for adenosine triphosphate. This is a molecule containing nitrogen. Attached to one end is a chain of three atom groups, called phos-phates. Energy is loaded into an ATP molecule when the end phosphate group is joined on. Disconnecting it unloads the energy. As ATP molecules are used up, new ones form, so there is always a supply at hand to power the cell's activities.

The cell lives by constantly storing and using energy, and by constantly rebuilding itself. Since food is needed for all this, what will happen if the food supply fails?

The protoplasm still goes on working. We know that a starving animal can stay alive for quite a while without food, but it loses weight. That is because its carbohydrates and fat are being consumed. Pro-tein, too, is burning. In the struggle for life, the cell fluid has begun to destroy itself.

Even when there is plenty of food, some portion of the cell fluid is always being destroyed. But at the same time it is being rebuilt. Activity goes on in both directions, building and breaking down, breaking down and building. And by endlessly changing, protoplasm stays the same—it lives.

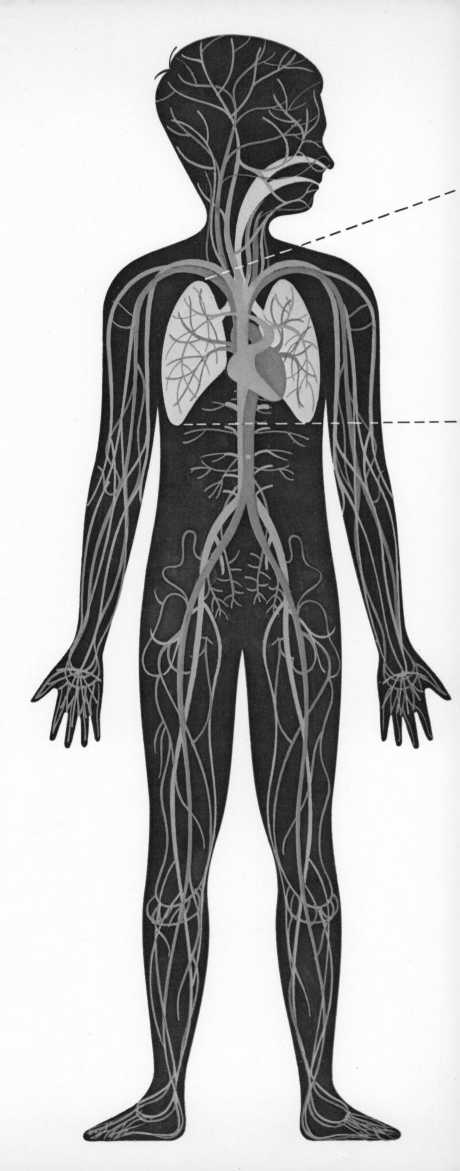

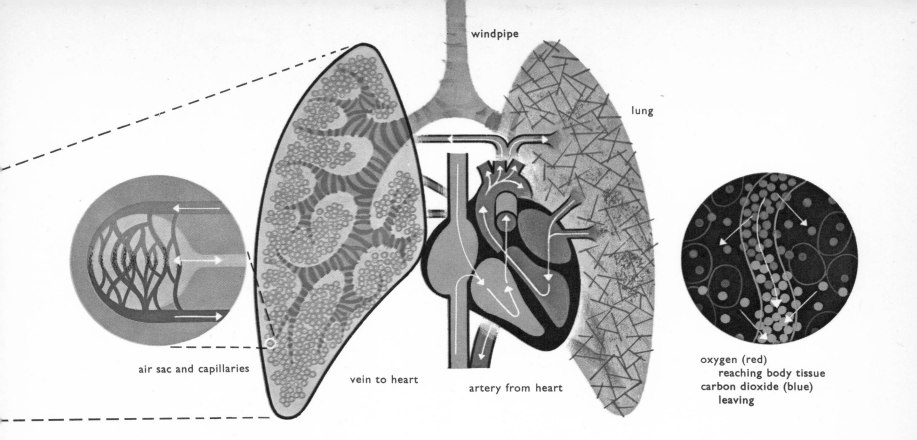

windpipe

lung

air sac and capillaries

vein to heart

artery from heart

oxygen (red)
reaching body tissue
carbon dioxide (blue)
leaving

Supplies for Your Millions of Cells

You, like an Amoeba, take in oxygen from the outside world and give back carbon dioxide. But unlike an Amoeba, you are separated from the world by a waterproof skin. And you cannot breathe through your skin.

A fish also has a skin that closes off its body tissues from the water. If the fish had a simple cell membrane instead of skin, oxygen would get through it. But the membrane would have too small an area to let in enough oxygen.

The fish's problem is solved by gills. These are thin sheets of tissue covered with membranes. The sheet arrangement gives a lot of surface. The sheets wave, and water is kept flowing over them. Plenty of oxygen comes in through the membranes.

In an air-breathing creature like yourself, lungs take the place of gills. Air enters them through the windpipe, which branches out into smaller and smaller tubes. These finally open into tiny sacs lined with membranes. The membranes are moist, so oxygen dissolves and seeps across them. Because there are thousands and thousands of air sacs, they make an enormous inside surface.

Beneath the membrane of each air sac are fine blood vessels—capillaries. Blood flows through them, transporting millions of red cells. These give your blood its colour. The red material is haemoglobin —a protein with some iron in its molecule. Haemoglobin has the very important job of taking oxygen from the air. Oxygen molecules are drawn through the air-sac membrane and into the capillaries. There the oxygen becomes loosely joined with the haemoglobin of the red cells.

Blood enriched with oxygen flows from your lungs to your heart, which pumps it through arteries to all parts of your body. The arteries pulse and keep it moving along. They divide into smaller and smaller vessels, leading to each tissue. There the vessels branch out into capillaries, through which blood circulates in the tissue. The capillaries connect with veins that carry the blood back towards the heart again.

The tissue cells and capillaries are bathed in a colourless fluid—lymph. When fresh blood arrives, oxygen leaves the haemoglobin and seeps through the capillary walls into the lymph. From there it is

37

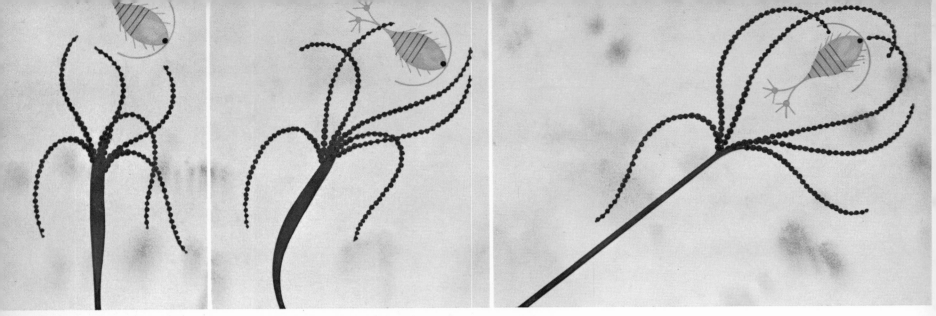

Hydra, a small pond animal, catching and swallowing a copepod

taken into the tissue cells. Carbon dioxide goes in the opposite direction. It passes from the cells to the lymph, into the capillaries and the blood, through the veins to the lungs, then out through the air sacs.

Water Transport

How does the food you eat become flesh and blood? How does any creature's food become a part of its body?

To begin with, food must be dissolved in order to cross cell membranes. This means it must be broken down—digested—into small molecules.

In many-celled animals, digestion usually takes place in a tube-shaped organ, the gut or intestine. You can see a very simple digestive tube in a creature called Hydra, a fresh-water relative of the jellyfishes and corals. It is often found on dead leaves at the bottom of a pond. Hydra looks like a half-inch piece of string. One end, coated with a gummy material, sticks to some surface. The free end appears to be frayed into fine threads, which wave about in the water.

When seen through a magnifying glass, Hydra turns out to be mainly a tube. The attached end of the tube is closed. The free end has a mouth through which food is taken in and waste is expelled. The

"threads" are tentacles around the mouth. Now and then they catch some small creature and draw it in. It is swallowed, and passes into the tube. Digestive enzymes trickle in from the cells lining the tube. When the food has been digested, the cells absorb it.

Worms have an improved model of the digestive tube. Each end is open. Food is taken in through the mouth, and waste material is discharged at the other end through an opening called the anus. When the gut is full of food, enzymes seep in and digest it into small molecules. These are absorbed through the gut wall and pass into the blood.

Large animals need a gut with a lot of inside surface. Several features provide this. In the first place, the tube is long. You, for example, have fifteen or twenty feet of looping, coiled gut. Its lining is covered with vast numbers of tiny projections called villi, which stick out like the threads on a bath towel. The membranes of the villi give a huge total surface. Fluids carrying digested food molecules wash against them and seep through, and then enter capillaries to become part of the blood.

Once in the blood stream, molecules of food are carried to all parts of the body. In each tissue, they go from the capillaries into the cells. Thus every cell in the body is provided with fuel and building material.

Earthworm, showing the digestive tube

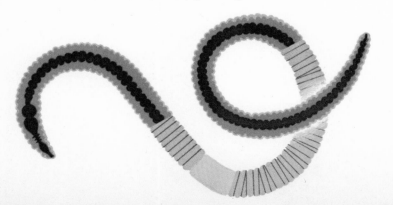

How Food Becomes Flesh

The working of every organ, tissue, and cell in your body depends on water. This precious fluid makes up most of the weight of blood, and forms

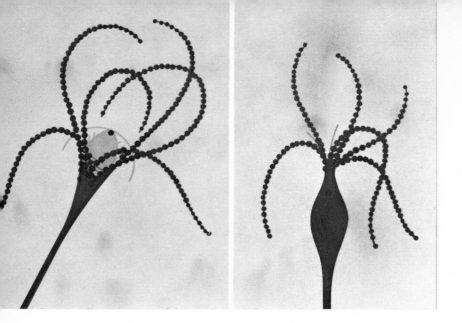

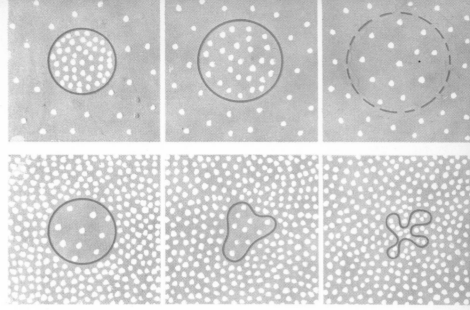

Red blood cell in water (above); in a sugar solution (below)

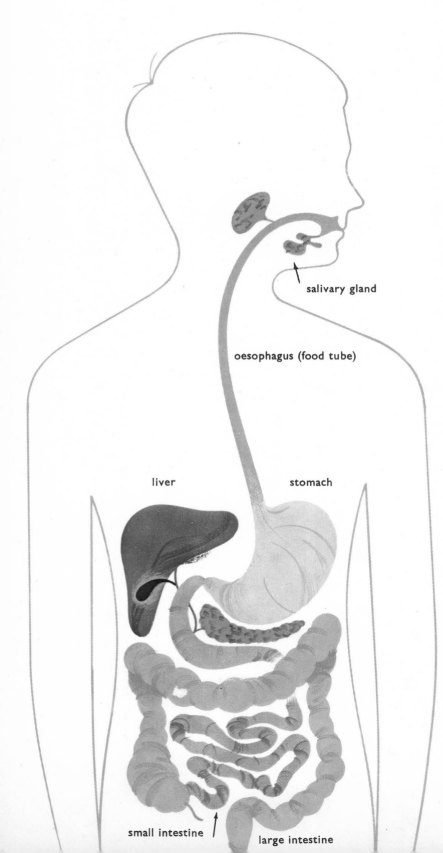

salivary gland

oesophagus (food tube)

liver

stomach

small intestine

large intestine

nine-tenths of protoplasm itself. Water delivers all the materials of life to your cells, and removes all their waste products.

To function well, your body must preserve its water balance. That is, the total water content must stay about the same, in spite of all gains and losses. And the water must be properly distributed.

Your body water is always crossing cell membranes. At each crossing, traffic must be regulated so that the amount of water entering a cell balances the amount leaving it. If more entered than left, the cell would swell up. If this happened to all the cells in a tissue, the tissue would blow up like a balloon. But if more water left the cells than entered, the tissue would shrivel.

We can arrange such disasters on a small scale under the microscope. Good cells to use as victims are the red blood cells. First we examine specimens floating in ordinary blood fluid—plasma. We see that each cell has the form of a disk—its ordinary and proper shape.

Then we remove the plasma with blotting paper, and drop plain water on to the cells. They swell, lose their disk shape, and bloat into balls. Some may burst.

With another batch of cells, we add a strong solution of table sugar. This makes each cell shrivel up into a little misshapen ghost of itself.

As you have guessed, there was trouble with the traffic of water across the cell membranes. The first batch of cells, gaining more water than they lost, enlarged. The second batch, losing more than they gained, shrank. What made these things happen?

39

Remember that a cell membrane is a network with many loopholes. Water and dissolved molecules of some substances slip through it almost as though the membrane were not there. But molecules of other substances – table sugar, for example – do not go through.

If we have a membrane with water on each side, about equal numbers of water molecules cross the membrane in each direction. But suppose the water on one side has a lot of dissolved molecules that do not cross membranes.

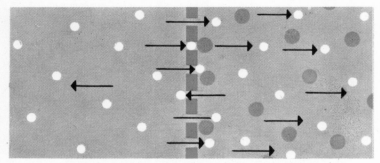

A membrane, with water on the left and sugar solution on the right

This was the case with the first batch of red cells. Outside each cell was plain water, but inside was protoplasm containing many kinds of molecules that do not cross membranes. On both sides, water molecules were hitting the membrane and getting through it. But on the inside, many dissolved molecules did not get through. These hits did not count. On the outside, more hits counted, since they were all made by water molecules. So water entered the cell faster than it left. In fact, it flooded in and bloated the cell.

In the second case, things were the other way around. The sugar solution had many molecules that do not cross membranes. The protoplasm inside the cells had fewer of them. This meant that on the inside more hits counted. Water left the cells faster than it entered, and the protoplasm shrank.

The Kidneys...Filtering Stations

Your blood is a solution, which must be regulated. This task is done by your kidneys. They are made up of some 39 miles of very fine coiled tubes, whose walls are membranes. In less than half an hour, every drop of blood in your body passes through the kidneys. All the water in your blood,

and all its dissolved food, salts, and other substances, are filtered by the tube membranes. Then 99% of the water and most of the dissolved substances are returned to the blood. One percent of the water leaves the blood for good, carrying along excess salts. Thus your kidneys keep your water balance just right.

They do another important job. They remove nitrogen compounds that come from the breakdown of proteins. These wastes, and the excess salts, are piped into the bladder. From there they leave the body as urine.

Clearly, your health and your very life depend on water with its cargo of dissolved substances. The stream of materials is always seeping through every tissue. Each second, it courses through your trunk blood vessels, trickles through millions of capillaries, and crosses the membranes of billions of cells. And so protoplasm is supplied and kept alive in every cell of your body.

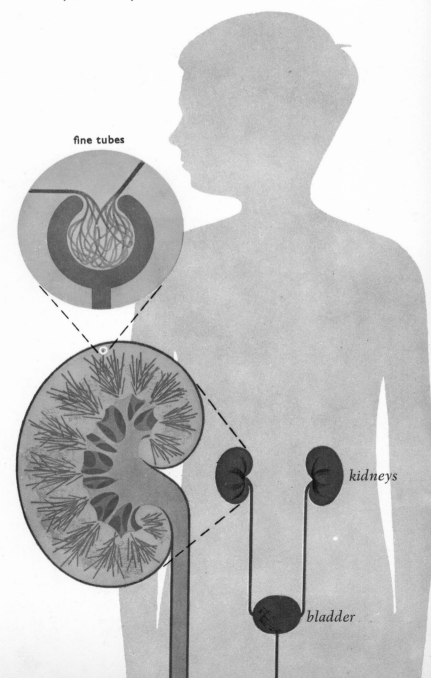

fine tubes

kidneys

bladder

The Wonder of Growth

What makes you grow? Food, of course - it forms new protoplasm, new cells, new tissue. But there is more to it than that.

Do you have pictures of yourself taken year after year since you were a baby? If you do, notice that different parts of your body grew at different rates. At first, your head grew more rapidly than the rest of you. After a few years, your trunk and limbs grew faster than your head. What will happen next? When you are a teen-ager, your arms and legs will stretch out to full length, and there will be many other changes.

You don't just grow—you develop, which means that your proportions change in an orderly way.

What Regulates Growth?

Several years ago, biologists in Japan were searching for ways to make crops grow better. They had heard of freak rice plants that farmers called "foolish seedlings" because they grew very thin and tall. The biologists examined these plants and found they were infected by a mould named Gibberella. Acids from this mould speeded the growth of the "foolish seedlings".

Perhaps the acids could be put to use. The biologists tried them on several kinds of plants. A lemon tree grew six times taller than usual. A cabbage plant, instead of forming a head, shot up fifteen feet tall, like Jack's beanstalk.

Such growth is useless, because it is disorderly. Plants do better by themselves.

Most of the plants you see every day—trees, for example—keep on growing as long as they live. Some of the giant sequoias in California have been growing for three or four thousand years.

Of course, trees do stop growing in winter. At temperatures below freezing point, sap cannot flow. Growing parts of a tree receive no water and nutrients for making new substance.

With the return of warm weather, sap flows again, bringing up food from the roots. Leaf buds drink in the nourishing fluid and swell until they burst. Then the young leaves unfold.

A small child and a grown-up have different proportions

How does it happen that growth goes on in just the right places, and at the proper rates? A century ago the great biologist Charles Darwin wondered about this. In one of his experiments he arranged the growing shoot of a seedling so that it received light from one side. In a few hours the stem bent towards the light. Darwin knew that this bending happened because cells on the shaded side of the stem grew and multiplied faster than those on the lighted side, and this pushed the stem towards the light.

Darwin supposed that growth of the stem was controlled by some special substance formed in the tip. Another scientist thought of a way to test this

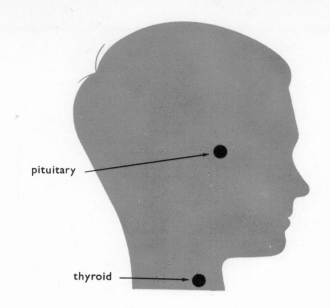

pituitary

thyroid

Two important glands

A growing plant bends towards the light

idea. He took a sprout and made a horizontal cut on one side of the stem, just below the tip. Into the cut he set a flake of mica. His idea was to stop any material formed in the tip from seeping down through that side of the stem. Then he arranged the sprout so that light reached it from the side opposite the cut. The stem should have bent towards the light, but didn't. Why not? It must have been because a substance made in the tip was shut off from the part of the stem that needed it.

Scientists have found that plants have a number of substances that regulate their growth. These are called hormones, meaning exciters. Different ones work on different parts of a plant. Several hormones have been extracted in pure form, and are sometimes used to encourage the growth of roots, buds, and fruits.

42

Giants, Dwarfs and Hormones

Most kinds of animals, like plants, grow as long as they live. This is generally true of turtles, snakes, crabs, lobsters, shrimps, snails, starfishes, worms, and countless others. The largest tuna in a school is an old fish that has been growing since it was a minnow. A giant squid, which may measure fifty feet from the tips of its tentacles to the end of its arrow-shaped tail, has probably been growing for a century or more.

Mammals and birds, unlike most other kinds of animals, grow to full size when they are young. And they grow faster in infancy. A human baby triples its weight by its first birthday. Never again will it grow at such a rate.

In human beings, as in all complicated animals, growth is regulated by a whole system of hormones. These are produced in special clumps of tissue

A giant tadpole and a dwarf frog; results of an experiment with glands and hormones

called glands. The glands discharge hormones into the blood stream, which carries them to the places where they are needed.

An important hormone comes from the thyroid glands. You have two of these, located in the sides of your neck. The work of the thyroid hormone has been studied in various animals, among them the frog. If a tadpole has its thyroid cut out, it stays a tadpole for the rest of its life, even though it may grow as large as an adult frog.

The development of another tadpole may be speeded up by giving it an extra dose of thyroid hormone. If this is done when the tadpole is tiny, it will turn into a frog no bigger than a fly.

Sometimes a baby is born with a thyroid that does not work. Years ago, a person with this trouble could not grow up properly. His body was dwarfed, and so was his brain and intelligence. But today, a child with an undeveloped thyroid is given the hormone he lacks. This helps him to grow up as he should.

Very important hormones come from the front part of a gland called the pituitary. In human beings, this is a pea-sized body attached to the base of the brain. Small though it is, the pituitary has a great influence on development. Its hormones travel around like messengers, signalling other glands to increase or cut down their own hormone production.

A tadpole that has had the front part of its pituitary removed never becomes a frog. When we examine such a tadpole, it turns out to have a thyroid ten times smaller than normal. Evidently, the thyroid is unable to grow without the proper signal from the pituitary.

Something like this can happen to a child. If his pituitary does not yield enough of its master hormones, bone growth is stunted, and the child becomes a dwarf. If too much growth hormone is produced, the bones grow so long that the child becomes a giant. Some day, no doubt, all such disorders of growth will be corrected by hormone treatment.

A python grows as long as it lives

How Tissues Grow

To watch tissues grow, it would be necessary to see their cells dividing and multiplying—a hard thing to do with a large creature.

It is easier to study the increase of one-celled organisms like bacteria. The biologist starts a "culture" with a few bacterial cells, or even one, which he places on some jellied food material in a dish. Each cell grows for a while, then divides into two. Later the two divide into four, the four into eight, and so on, until the organisms have become a colony, forming a stain on the jelly.

Why not culture human cells in the same way? Certain investigators have tried this, and find it no harder than raising bacteria. They take single cells from some tissue like liver, kidney, lung, skin, or bone, place them on a jelly, and watch the results.

In this way, nearly every kind of human cell has been grown in culture. After a colony is started, a census is kept to see how long the cells take to grow and divide. When kept warm and properly nourished, they double their number in about eighteen hours. Each cell spends most of this time growing. Then growth stops, the cell begins to divide, and in forty-five minutes there are two new cells in its place.

In your body, cells don't ordinarily divide every eighteen hours. If they did, you would double in size once a day. Instead, division goes on in an orderly way, as new cells are needed.

A sexless Hydra budding

In certain emergencies, cells can and do multiply at their maximum rate. You have seen results of this. At some time or other you have cut your finger, then waited for it to heal. As it does, cells around the cut divide and increase rapidly. New generations of cells replace the ones that were destroyed, and in a short time the wound is healed without leaving a trace.

Of the thousands of billion cells in your body, many millions are lost each day. The dried up remains of skin cells are rubbed away as tiny flakes. Other cells are removed from the lining of your intestine by food masses passing through it. In various organs like the liver and kidneys, worn-out cells dissolve, leaving their materials to be used again by living cells near by.

All in all, the cells that you lose each day amount to one or two pounds of your weight. This loss is made up by the splitting and multiplication of millions of other cells. And so you keep on changing just to stay the same.

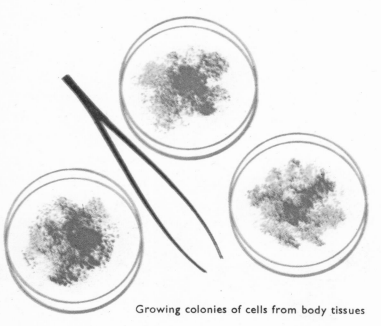

Growing colonies of cells from body tissues

Male Hydra and sperm cells   Female Hydra with eggs

Sex and Mating

In the course of its lifetime, a young plant or animal becomes an adult, and then is able to start having young of its own. Growing up seems just a step towards reproduction.

Among micro-organisms, methods of reproduction are fairly simple. Amoeba just divides into two little copies of itself. One-celled plants and bacteria do the same.

Things are more complicated with larger creatures. Take what happens to Hydra, the "frayed bit of string". Every now and then, Hydra sprouts a "bud", which soon becomes a new little Hydra joined to the old. Once the offspring has tentacles and a mouth, it breaks away to live by itself.

Hydra continues budding in this way so long as its pond stays fairly warm. But in autumn, it stops budding and begins to reproduce by another method. Along its body, bulges of two sorts develop. Each produces a special kind of cell. In one, a single large cell forms. This is an egg. In the other, many tiny cells form. These are sperms.

Each sperm cell has a little tail. The sperms are released into the water, and swim by fluttering their tails. Several find their way to an egg. One enters it and mixes with the egg substance. This fertilises the egg and makes it start developing into a new Hydra.

In some types of Hydra, one animal produces eggs; another, sperms. This divides the population into two sexes. The egg producers are females; the sperm producers are males. So it is with the "higher" animals—the more complicated ones. They are divided into sexes, and the thing that makes each one either male or female is the kind of reproductive cell it produces.

45

Fertilisation – A Problem

Reproduction by sexes brings a complication. Eggs and sperms must meet, and this seldom happens easily.

Among many creatures of the sea, males and females do not seek one another. A starfish does not recognise another starfish's sex. Yet starfishes reproduce. Nature has given them glands that pour out reproductive cells in vast numbers, and clouds of them drift in the water. Millions of eggs and sperms die without meeting. But since there are so many, a few among the sperms are bound to find eggs and fertilise them. The eggs then develop into tiny swimmers, which will later settle down on the sea bed and become starfishes.

This system works in the sea, where eggs and sperms can stay alive long enough for some of them to meet. But on land things are different. If cells were exposed to the air without protection, they would immediately dry up and die.

Flowering plants reproduce by means of male and female cells, which are well protected. The egg cells (ovules) are sheltered in a little case inside the flower. The male cells are stored in flecks of pollen.

The garden pea plant is one of those that fertilises itself with its own pollen. Grasses shed pollen that the wind carries from plant to plant. Oak and birch trees also spread their pollen through the air.

Plants with bright and scented flowers attract insects and other small creatures. Bees visit flowers to gather pollen and sip nectar. During such visits, their bodies become dusted with pollen, which they carry from flower to flower. Without knowing it, the bees and other nectar-gatherers help the plants to reproduce.

The Riddle of the Egg with a Shell

Beetles and roaches lay eggs that are enclosed in tough, wax-coated shells or cases that keep them from drying up.

But how is an armour-clad egg to be fertilised? Not after it is laid, certainly, for then a sperm would be shut out by the shell. In any case the sperm would die if it were exposed to the air.

Life story of a plant: from flower to seed to new plant

Moths and fireflies find their mates in the dark

Beetles solve this riddle by mating, for which they have special organs. The male organ fits into the female, and fluid containing sperm cells goes from the male into the body of the female. There the sperms are safe, and fertilise the eggs before they have been closed up in shells.

Since the eggs of birds and reptiles also are shell-covered, they too must be fertilised inside the female, before shells form around them. So the animals mate, and sperms reach the eggs in time.

Finding Mates in the Dark

We have been talking as though it were quite a simple matter for animals to find mates. But is it? Think of a small beetle living by itself in the big world. Suppose it hides for safety during the day, and goes about mainly at night. How is it to find a mate?

You have seen fireflies twinkling in the dusk on a summer evening. The firefly is a beetle with special glands that help to produce light. At the right time, the light flashes automatically.

Male fireflies go flying about in the dark, giving flashes like signals of tiny planes. They are signals, surely enough, but signals for female fireflies.

The females just sit quietly on stems of grass, waiting. When a male flashes near a female, she flashes back. Changing course, he flies towards her. After a few more signals back and forth, the male finds his way to the female, and they mate.

Of course, the fireflies don't plan what they are doing, nor think about it at all. They act by instinct. This is a kind of built-in memory inherited from ancestors who have behaved in the same way for thousands or millions of years.

The signal system works because male fireflies always behave as males, and females as females. It wouldn't work so well if both sexes flew, or both sat and waited. Then males would meet males half the time, and females would meet females. Only by chance would the opposite sexes find one another.

Since most insects have no signal lights, they can't use their eyes to find mates in the dark. Many kinds of large moths depend on their sense of smell, which is located in the feathery antennae on their heads. In this case, too, the female sits and waits. She has a strong scent, which drifts out on the night air. Somewhere, perhaps quite far away, a male is aroused by the scent, which guides him to a mate he has never seen.

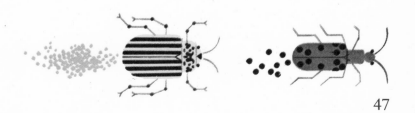

47

The Courtship of Birds

Songbirds seem to have every possible help for recognising the opposite sex and finding mates. Apart from an easily distinguished song, each sex ordinarily has its own markings and plumage which identify it as male or female.

The blackcap is a grey bird. Only the male is marked with the characteristic black cap, the female having a brown patch on her head instead. As with most birds, she is altogether less gaily plumaged than her mate.

The handsome male bird puts on a special dress display while courting. He raises his head feathers, puffs out his body feathers, droops his wings and vigorously agitates his tail, pouring out his finest melody the while. The blackcap has a particularly delightful song and is sometimes known as the nightingale of the north. Soon another listener hears his song. She known it is for her. Before long, the birds mate, build a nest, have eggs and hatch out a brood.

The blackcap's song plays a part in courtship

As light serves the firefly, and scent the moth, sound serves other insects. From spring to autumn, crickets, katydids, grasshoppers, and cicadas chirp in chorus. They sing mostly at night, and their songs are love songs.

The males make the noise, but not with voices, for they have none. The katydid's instrument is his outer set of wings, which he scrapes against one another to produce the sound. The grasshopper rubs his long hind leg across his wing, as a fiddler draws his bow across the strings of his fiddle.

A song would be useless if there were no ears to hear it. The grasshopper's "ears" are lined up along the sides of its body. The cricket and katydid have hearing organs on their forelegs. To a female listener, only one song is appealing—the song of the male of her own kind. Picking it out from all the others, she makes her way unerringly to her future mate.

48

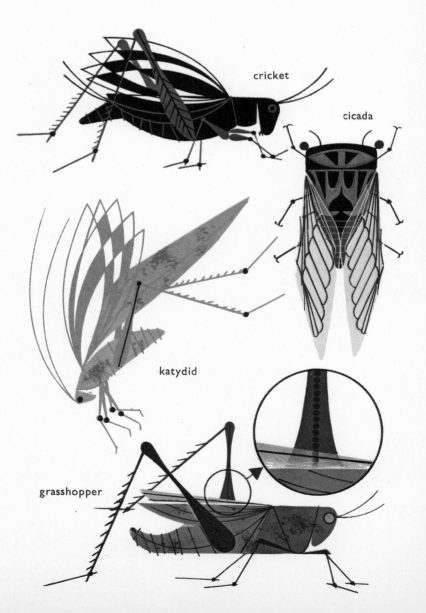

cricket

cicada

katydid

grasshopper

The male helps to build the nest, which is made of dry grass and lined with finer grass and hairs. Once the eggs have been laid, he helps to incubate them and both birds will care for the nestlings when they have hatched out. Sometimes, if danger threatens, the resourceful blackcap will feign injury to protect the young birds, and by this means, draw the enemy away from his nest.

He or She?

Among birds of the sea, male and female usually look alike and have similar voices and calls. You can't tell whether a gull is male or female, and neither can a gull, from looks alone. To another sea bird, the gannet, one gannet looks like every other.

Sex doesn't matter during most of the year. But at mating time everything changes, and the all-important question to every bird is, "Who is who?"

Gannets by the thousands settle at the mating and nesting place. Each male in the colony takes the best spot he can find, and guards it against any intruder. If a neighbour comes too close, he threatens and scolds and jabs with his bill.

Will the stranger retreat or stay? If it retreats, it is a male, or perhaps a female not yet ready for mating. If it stays, it is a female ready to mate.

Then comes courtship. The male gannet offers gifts to the female—bits of twig, seaweed, or food. As part of their courtship, the partners perform a ceremonial dance, clashing their bills together. This helps get them ready to mate. And it makes them so well acquainted that from then on they will be able to recognise one another among the other birds in the colony.

Of all the creatures that mate, mammals certainly are the most interesting to us, since we ourselves belong to the mammal family. But we'll save this part of the story until later, when we tell how mammals care for their young and start them off in the world.

Gannets choosing mates at their nesting place

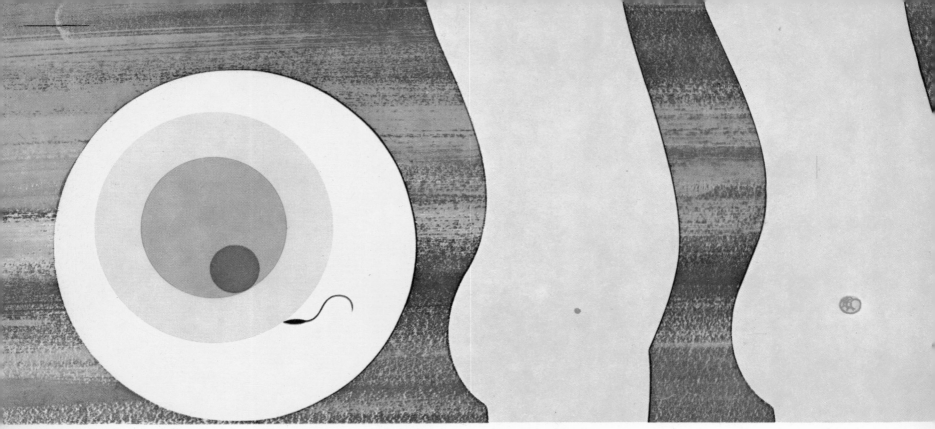

Human egg and sperm cells, magnified   Beginning of pregnancy   Second month

Before Birth

Fish and frog, bird and bee, mouse and man—each begins life as a fertilised egg cell. The egg gives no hint of the creature that is to come from it. The human egg, which is of microscopic size, looks like the eggs of many mammals. Like all animal cells, it is a droplet of protoplasm containing a nucleus and enclosed in a membrane. Nothing about it suggests its wonderful power to develop into a human being.

A woman usually produces mature egg cells for forty years of her life. They form in the two female sex glands, the ovaries. About every four weeks an egg ripens in one of the ovaries and leaves it to enter a winding tube.

After a woman and man have mated, there may be sperm cells in the tube, and one of the sperm cells may fertilise the egg. Soon the fertilised egg passes down the tube and enters a sac with thick walls. This is the uterus, the sheltered place where a baby grows and develops.

By the time the egg has reached the uterus, it has already begun to develop. It has split into two cells, the two have split into four, the four into eight, and so on, until the egg is a little clump of cells. In this stage and the ones that follow, it is called an embryo. The embryo becomes attached to the lining of the uterus, where it will stay and grow for nine months, receiving food and oxygen from the mother's blood stream.

It may happen that two eggs ripen at about the same time and both become fertilised. Then the mother, instead of having one baby, has twins.

Among other mammals, too, the young develop

Fertilised chicken's egg, second day   Fourth day   Seventh day

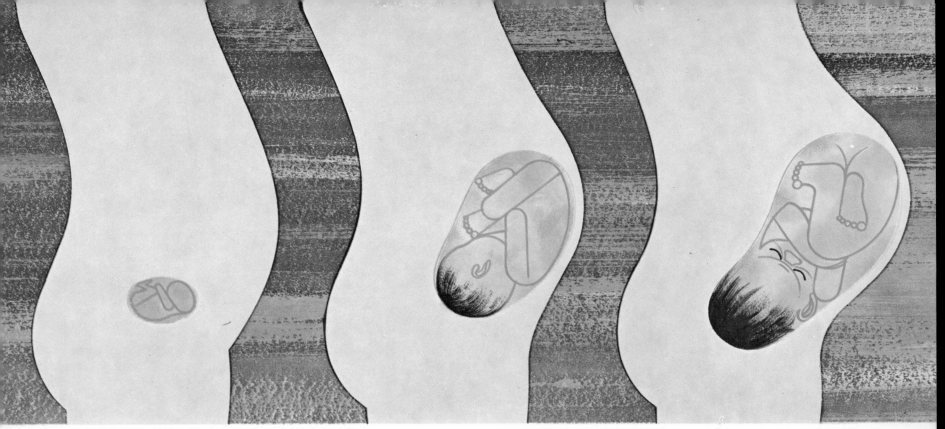

Fourth month   Sixth month   Ninth month

inside the mother's body. In the female cat, dog, rabbit, or mouse, a number of eggs usually ripen at about the same time. Several of them are likely to become fertilised, so the mother produces several young at once.

Most animals do not give birth to fully formed young. Instead, the mother lays eggs, and the embryos develop in them. The egg of a frog, bird, or turtle is large compared to a mammal's egg. It must be large, to hold enough food for the embryo until it becomes a young creature ready to hatch. The big yolk of a bird or reptile egg is the embryo's food.

Frog and fish eggs have no shells; these are unnecessary for eggs laid in water. But bird and reptile eggs, since they are laid on land, need shells to keep them from drying up.

The part of a hen's egg that develops into the embryo is just a tiny spot on the yolk. You won't notice it in the eggs you eat, for they are not fertilised. When an egg is fertilised, the spot becomes darker and easier to see. It is just a droplet of protoplasm containing the cell nucleus.

How can this bit of matter become a creature with a head, body, wings, feet, and feathers? How can it develop into the different cells and tissues that make a chick's skin, bone, heart, blood, and brain? Biologists have wondered how this miracle happens, and have tried to find out.

The First Stages of Development

In the first few hours of life, all fertilised eggs go through the same changes. Because of this, biologists can study one kind of egg and learn a great deal about the development of all kinds, including the human egg.

Frogs' eggs are often used because they are easy to handle and watch. In the spring, clusters of them can be found in ponds. At other times of the year they can be obtained from frogs kept in laboratories.

Fourteenth day

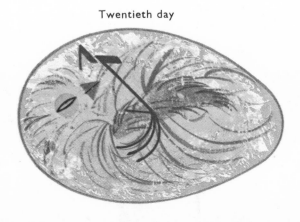

Twentieth day

Twenty-first day

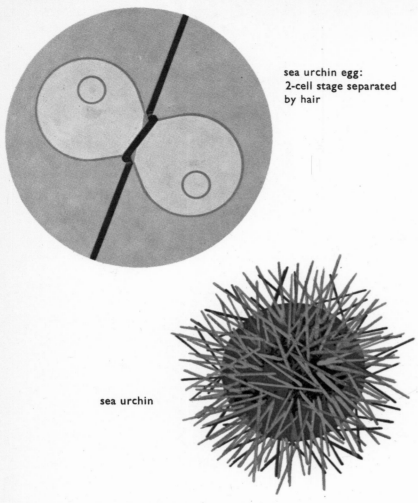

sea urchin egg:
2-cell stage separated
by hair

sea urchin

How Hans Driesch obtained two sea urchins from one
egg cell

vide into sixteen, the sixteen into thirty-two, and so on. Continuing to divide, the cells spread outward, so as to leave an open space in the centre. Thus they form a hollow sphere made of one layer of cells.

At first, the outside of the sphere is fairly regular. Then a dent forms at one point on its surface. As the cells go on dividing, new ones are added to the layer. They crowd against cells at the edge of the dent, making them slide over the edge. Pushing inward, the cells make the dent deeper. In a little while the sphere looks like a tiny rubber ball with one side pressed in. The dent continues to deepen, becoming a tube-like hollow. This is the beginning of the body cavity, which will contain the heart, stomach, intestines and other organs.

So far the unhatched animal—the embryo—is just a dented ball of cells. All of them look alike. But experiments have shown that the cells are no longer all the same. Biologists have cut pieces from different parts of the ball and let them grow separately to see what would happen. The pieces develop differently. For example, cells from one region become stomach tissue; those from another region become nerve.

When Differences Start

Just when do various regions of the embryo start to become different from one another? Around 1890, biologists were looking for the answer to this question. One of them, Hans Driesch, experimented with eggs of the sea urchin. This is a small, spiny creature that crawls along the ocean floor. Driesch waited for a fertilised egg to divide into two cells. Then, using a human hair, he performed the delicate operation of separating the cells.

A hour or two after a frog's egg has been fertilised, dramatic changes begin. At the top of the egg, the surface folds inward, making a crease. The crease spreads down both sides of the egg to the bottom. Cutting inward, it divides the egg in half. This makes two new cells, which stay side by side.

Other divisions follow rapidly. The two cells split from top to bottom, making four smaller ones. Then the four split across, making eight. The eight di-

A frog's egg, magnified. How it divides and develops.

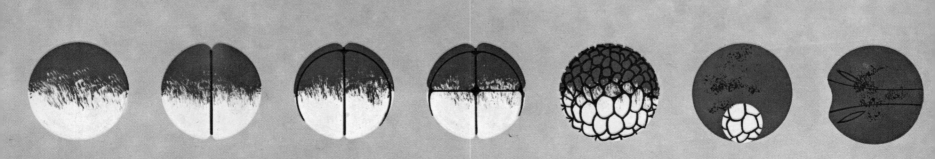

What would the separated cells do? Would each become half an animal? If so, this would show that the two cells were already different. But nothing of the sort happened. Instead, a whole and perfect young animal developed from each cell. This meant that the two cells were entirely alike.

Sometimes the cells formed by the first division of an egg separate naturally. This may happen to a human egg, so both cells become embryos, which develop into twins. Since these twins come from a single fertilised egg, they are quite alike—so similar that they are called "identical twins".

Experimenting with salamanders, Hans Driesch not only made twins, he made quadruplets. He did this by waiting for the second division of the egg. Then there were four cells, which he separated. He managed to do the same after the third division, when there were eight cells, and after the fourth division, when there were sixteen. And in each case he obtained complete animals from all the cells— even from the sixteen!

This showed that regions of the embryo do not start to become different until some time after the fourth division. But just when and where does the process begin?

This problem was taken up by Hans Spemann, a German biologist of great skill and imagination. He wondered if portions of embryos could be cut out and transplanted so as to make certain tissues grow in the wrong places.

For his experiment, Spemann used two embryos of the common newt, which is a salamander. Both embryos were allowed to reach the hollow sphere stage. Then, from one of them, Spemann cut a part that would normally develop into brain; from the other he took a part that would ordinarily become stomach tissue. The fragments were transplanted from one embryo to the other. In one, future brain tissue was grafted into the future stomach region; in the other, future stomach tissue was grafted into the future brain region. The two grafts took, and the embryos continued to grow. In fact, they developed quite normally, as though there had been no grafts at all. The transplanted brain cells became stomach tissue, and the transplanted stomach tissue became brain.

What guided the transplanted cells in their development? Over and over again, Spemann watched egg cells divide and shape themselves into hollow spheres. He watched the forming of the dent, and the motion of cells that glided over its edge, pushing the dent inward. Perhaps this region, with all its activity and movement, was the place to look for the guiding influence, whatever it was. Spemann called it the "organiser".

from tadpole to frog

In his next experiment, Spemann cut the edge of the dent from one embryo and grafted it into another. The result was an embryo with two dents—one its own, and one which developed where the graft had been placed. Each dent grew inward, and each formed a separate body cavity. Development went on around each cavity, so that the embryo became two animals, complete but joined together.

Apparently, cells around the dent produce some chemical that acts on neighbouring cells and causes them to develop into a body cavity.

Hans Spemann's experiment: making one embryo develop into two salamanders

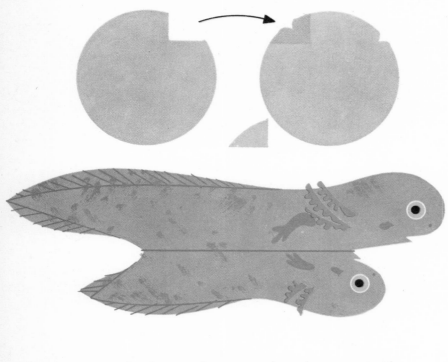

Another experiment: two salamanders grow up with eyes that do not match

But this is only the beginning. From then on, the embryo continues folding and gathering into new shapes, while new types of cells form new tissues and organs. At each stage, it seems, chemical "organisers" go to work just when they are needed to start and guide the next step.

Chemicals that Shape an Unborn Creature

Sometimes, organising substances from the embryo of one kind of animal will work on an embryo of another kind. The organiser that controls the forming of a chick's brain will make a rabbit embryo grow some extra brain tissue in a place where it doesn't belong.

In a well-known experiment, tissue was cut from the mouth region of a frog embryo and grafted on to a salamander embryo in the place where the mouth would form. The salamander developed a mouth, but it was a frog's mouth!

A similar experiment was done with two kinds of salamander embryos, one a big type, the other small. Tissue that would develop into an eye was cut from each embryo and grafted on to the other. Each embryo grew into a salamander that was normal in every way except that its eyes did not match. The big salamander had one little eye, and the little salamander had one big eye.

What do such results show? Evidently, the egg of each kind of animal has special substances of its own to guide its future development. When the egg divides and new cells form, these substances are passed on to them. Going from one generation of cells to the next, they work as master chemicals, producing other chemicals to guide each new turn in development. Every little change, every bit of growth, comes at just the right time, so it fits with other changes going on in different parts of the embryo.

The system works well, causing the young one to develop properly. Mistakes seldom happen, and these are usually not serious. Perhaps something goes slightly wrong in one young creature in a thousand. One frog or one baby may be born with an unusual trait, like six fingers instead of five. But of the other 999, each is as it should be, a creature of marvellous perfection.

Why You Are You

Why are you the person you are? Why do you have a face of a certain shape; eyes, hair, and skin of a certain colour; and all your other traits?

Friends of the family like to give their own views about your features. You got your nose from your father, eyes from your mother, this trait from one grandparent, that trait from another.

There seems to be something to this, judging from the pictures in your family album. Your ancestors did have certain features that appeared again and again, and some of them have reappeared in you. Yet everyone in the family is different. You yourself are different from your brother or sister—unless you happen to be an identical twin. You are also different from your parents. Some of your traits are like theirs, but many are different. Perhaps both your father and mother have brown eyes but you have blue. This often happens.

The Puzzle of Inheritance

Questions something like this come up in the breeding of plants and animals. Breeders, as you know, select certain plants and animals to be parents of the next generation. For example, they pick out dogs with desirable traits, in order to have these traits in the pups. Selective breeding has been carried on for centuries, and now, because of it, we have many fine types of dogs, poultry, cattle, grains, vegetables, and fruits.

In early days, breeders of plants and animals often failed to get the results they wanted. Some desired trait of the parents would not appear in the young. What was the matter? Why didn't the line "breed true"?

The trouble was, nobody knew how traits are inherited. Many scientists had tried to discover the secret of heredity, but had failed. This did not discourage a certain determined experimenter, Gregor Mendel, who was a monk and schoolteacher in the city of Brno in Czechoslovakia. He also worked hard at the hobby he loved—breeding plants in his monastery garden.

For his experiments on heredity, Mendel chose several strains of the common garden pea. This was a good choice. The pea plant is self-fertilising. Before the flower opens, its own pollen grains, from which sperm cells develop, fertilise its egg cells. Pollen from outside hardly ever gets into a flower in time to fertilise the eggs, so different plants do not pollinate one another. Because of this, a strain ordinarily stays pure and breeds true—it keeps the same traits from generation to generation.

When Mendel was sure he had pure strains, he began to cross-fertilise them by cutting open their flowers and bringing pollen from a plant of one strain to a plant of another. He bred and cross-bred his peas for eight years, keeping a record of more than ten thousand plants and their seeds. And through this painstaking work he discovered the laws of heredity. They are the same for plants and for people. When you know these laws, you will know how you inherited your own traits.

Nature's Number Game

Mendel began by crossing a strain of peas that had yellow seeds with one that had green seeds. Using an artist's brush, he transferred pollen from a green-seed plant to flowers of a yellow-seed plant. Then he waited for seed pods to form from the flowers, and collected the pods.

The seeds, of course, contained embryos—tiny young plants of the next generation. Since the seeds and their embryos were products of cross-breeding, Mendel called them hybrids, which means crossbreeds.

When Mendel took the seeds from their pods, he had a surprise. Every one was yellow. What

Gregor Mendel transferring pollen from one flower to another

56

had happened? Why had the green-seed trait disappeared?

Mendel planted the hybrid seeds and from them raised 258 plants. They blossomed, were allowed to fertilise themselves with their own pollen, then went to seed. These seeds were the second hybrid generation. When Mendel opened the pods, he found they contained green as well as yellow seeds!

This could mean only one thing. The seeds of the first hybrid generation, though they were yellow, contained some "factor" that passed on to seeds of the second hybrid generation, causing some to be green.

Mendel counted 8,023 seeds of the second hybrid generation. Of these, 6,022 were yellow and 2,001 were green, so the ratio was about three yellow to one green. What did this ratio mean? Mendel had an idea, but he was not hasty. He wanted more facts.

How Heredity Works

Mendel raised plants from the green seeds, let them pollinate themselves, and collected the seeds of the third generation. All were green. In following generations, the green-seed plants bred true. But when a third generation was raised from the yellow seeds, again there were green seeds as well as yellow.

Now Mendel saw a clear meaning in his figures. It is explained in the diagrams on this page.

Mendel supposed that each sperm and egg cell carried only one factor for seed colour, either yellow or green. When a sperm and an egg united, each contributed its factor to the resulting seed, giving it a pair of factors. In a pure yellow-seed strain, both factors were for yellow, so the seed was yellow. In a green-seed strain, both factors were for green, so the seed was green (Diagram one).

When the green and yellow strains were cross-pollinated, each sperm and egg contributed a different factor to the seed they formed (Diagram two). As a result, this seed contained both a yellow and a green colour factor. Yet the seed was yellow, as were all the rest of the first hybrid generation. This meant that the factor for yellow was stronger, or dominant, since it gave this trait to the seed. The factor for green, being weaker, or recessive, was hidden by the yellow trait.

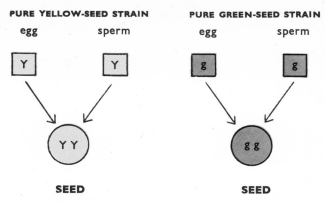

Diagram 1. Breeding pure strains. Y is the factor for yellow seed colour; g is the factor for green seed colour. Each sex cell gives one factor to the seed, so the seed has a pair. In the yellow-seed strain, the pair is yellow-yellow. In the green-seed strain, it is green-green.

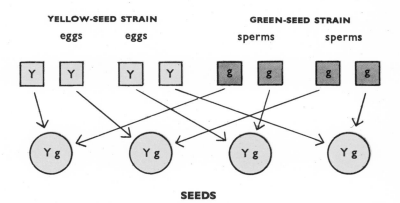

Diagram 2. Crossing a yellow-seed strain and a green-seed strain. This gives hybrid seeds (cross-breeds). Every seed is yellow, but contains the green as well as the yellow seed-colour factor.

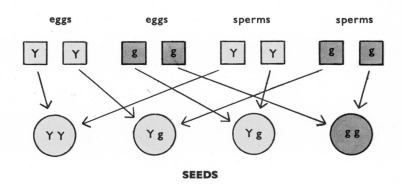

Diagram 3. Breeding a second generation of hybrids. In one-quarter of the seeds, the pair of seed-colour factors is green-green, so these seeds are green. In the rest, the pairs are yellow-yellow and yellow-green, so these seeds are yellow.

57

But the green factor was still there. Passing on to the second generation, it caused one-quarter of the seeds to be green. *Diagram three* shows the cause of this three-to-one ratio. In about half the sex cells of plants of the first generation, the factor for seed colour was yellow; in the other half, it was green. When the sex cells united, they could make three possible combinations of factors: yellow-yellow, yellow-green, and green-green.

That was just what they did, so the seeds of the second generation contained all three kinds of pairs. It is easy to see why there were more yellow seeds. Those with the yellow-yellow combination were yellow, of course. So were those with yellow-green, since the factor for yellow dominated over green and made the seeds yellow. Only a seed with two green factors could be green.

Now you can understand why a brown-eyed father and mother may have a blue-eyed child. Brown and blue eye colours are like the yellow and green colours of peas. They are caused by different hereditary factors. Both the father and mother inherited the factor for brown eyes, but in each of them it was paired with the factor for blue eyes. Brown is dominant over blue, so it made their eyes brown. In the forming of their sex cells, just one factor went into each sperm and egg. Some sex cells

had the factor for brown eyes, others the factor for blue. The particular sperm and egg that united to make the child both happened to contain the factor for blue eyes, so his eyes were blue.

This all seems simple and logical now, but it took Mendel's clear thinking and careful experiments to show how heredity works. He checked his results over and over again. He crossed strains of peas that had several opposed traits, among them yellow and green seed colour, different pod shapes, and different positions of flowers on the plant. And it turned out that the hybrids of the second generation had all these traits in every possible combination. But for each pair of opposed traits, the ratio was always three dominant to one recessive.

Mendel's discoveries were published in a scientific journal that few people read. Biologists of the time did not study his work, so the discoveries were forgotten before they ever became really known and understood.

What were Mendel's "hereditary factors"? Neither he nor anyone else had ever seen them. Were they particles of some sort in sex cells and seeds? The question remained unanswered until long after Mendel's death. Finally the mysterious factors were discovered, and scientists found that Mendel's work explained the factors' behaviour.

Why brown-eyed parents may have a blue-eyed child

How Cells Pass on Inheritance

In the 1880's and 90's, biologists were using their microscopes to watch living cells in action. Walther Flemming, in Germany, examined cells in the transparent tails and gills of salamanders. He saw cells in various stages of division, and caught glimpses of strange, complicated events going on inside them. How could he get a clear picture of these events?

After testing various dyes and stains, Flemming picked out some that would colour structures in the cells and make them visible. Soon he had a large collection of stained tissue specimens. They contained many dividing cells, with their structures arranged in various ways. Evidently, Flemming had caught the cells in different stages of division. By putting the stages in the right order, he managed to calculate what happens when a cell divides.

Today, the whole process has been caught in motion pictures. When they are speeded up, events that really take about an hour unfold before our eyes in a few minutes.

The drama begins in the nucleus. At first the protoplasm is still. Then swarms of little grains link up, forming a loose tangle of threads. These structures take a stain that makes them easy to see, so they are called chromosomes, which means coloured bodies. Gradually, the chromosomes shorten and thicken. Each now looks like a transparent fibre with a thread running through it. At first the thread is single; then, somehow, it makes a copy of itself and becomes double.

The chromosomes have various shapes, resembling the letters V, J, and I. For each one, there is a twin, for the chromosomes come in pairs. Every kind of animal and plant has a definite number of

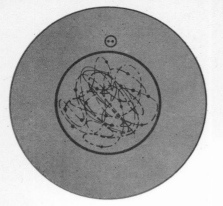 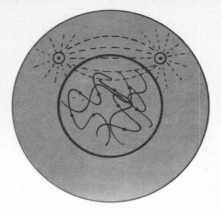 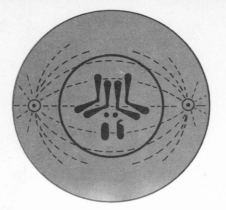 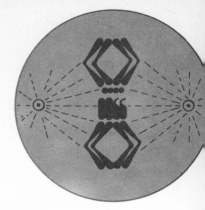

In the fruit fly, 4 pairs of chromosomes form. Each chromosome splits. Result: 16 chromosomes

chromosome pairs. A fruit fly has four, a tomato plant has twelve, a human being has twenty-three pairs.

While the chromosomes are shaping, the membrane around the nucleus dissolves and disappears. At the same time (in an animal cell) two little globes float to opposite ends of the cell. Between them, a spindle-shaped figure gathers, made of threads of protoplasm.

The chromosomes, moving like figures in a dance, gather on a plane across the middle of the spindle. Now comes the climax of the dance. Each chromosome splits lengthwise, and its two halves move away from one another. When all are divided, they form two sets. In each set, the chromosomes appear to be pulled by threads of the spindle, which makes them move in opposite directions.

When the two chromosome sets are in opposite halves of the cell, the cell membrane folds in and separates the halves. In each half, the chromosomes become a loose tangle of threads, as they were in the original cell. A membrane forms around each collection, making a nucleus. Now each half-cell is itself a cell, with a copy of the old cell's chromosomes.

The Making of Sex Cells

Having learned this much about tissue cells, biologists turned their attention to sex cells. They wondered if sperms and eggs also are formed through cell division. To find out, they took living cells from the sex glands of frogs and other creatures, and watched them under the microscope.

It turned out that these cells divide and re-divide several times, and the final products are sex cells. But this is not all. In the course of the various divisions, something quite unusual happens. The chromosomes become single instead of paired, and this

reduces them to half the usual number. In the human species, which has twenty-three chromosome pairs, a sex cell has just twenty-three single chromosomes.

After long years of work, biologists managed to find out how the number of chromosomes in sex cells comes to be cut in half. In the next to last division, the chromosomes go through their dance in a special way. The members of each pair drift together and join side by side; then the pairs line up across the middle of the cell.

The division that follows is not a dividing and doubling of single chromosomes, but simply a disjoining of the pairs. The partners separate and drift apart. This makes two sets of single chromosomes that go to opposite halves of the cell. The membrane folds in, and the cell is divided into two new ones. Each has single chromosomes instead of pairs.

Though the chromosomes in a sperm or unferti-

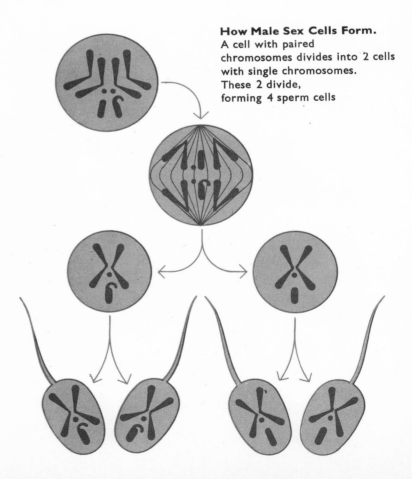

How Male Sex Cells Form. A cell with paired chromosomes divides into 2 cells with single chromosomes. These 2 divide, forming 4 sperm cells

60

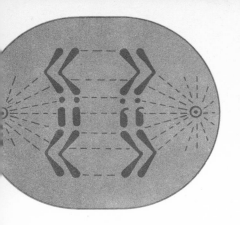
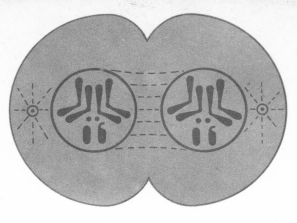
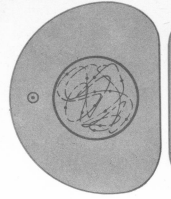
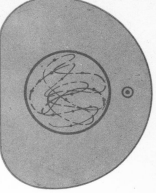

The chromosomes gather in 2 sets

The sets separate; the cell divides

lised egg are single, they are double in a fertilised egg. It is not hard to guess why. When a sperm and egg unite, their single chromosomes combine to make pairs.

When these things were first observed, biologists wondered what part chromosomes played in heredity. Mendel's forgotten report was studied, and the scientists realised that the chromosomes behaved just as Mendel had said the hereditary factors must behave. They came in pairs, were separated in the sex cells, and combined in the fertilised egg. The chromosomes were Mendel's hereditary factors!

It soon became clear that chromosomes are not single units of heredity. There are too few of them to account for all the traits a creature inherits. The chromosomes therefore must be collections of many units.

What, then, is the single unit of heredity? The name gene has been given to it, but what *is* a gene?

Biologists have searched the chromosomes for it, and at last their search is leading somewhere.

Search for the Gene

For the next step forward in the study of inheritance, scientists can thank a little creature they found in the dustbin. This is the common fruit fly. It feeds on things like rotten bananas, and lays eggs that hatch into wormlike grubs.

It would be hard to find a more convenient animal to use in experiments on heredity. The fruit fly breeds rapidly, and can be reared easily in jars. It has only four pairs of chromosomes. In some tissues of the grub, each cell grows to giant size, which makes it easy to observe. Instead of dividing, such a cell just grows and grows. The chromosomes divide and increase, but do not separate. Their threads merely stick together in one bundle.

The fruit fly, which has been used in many experiments on heredity

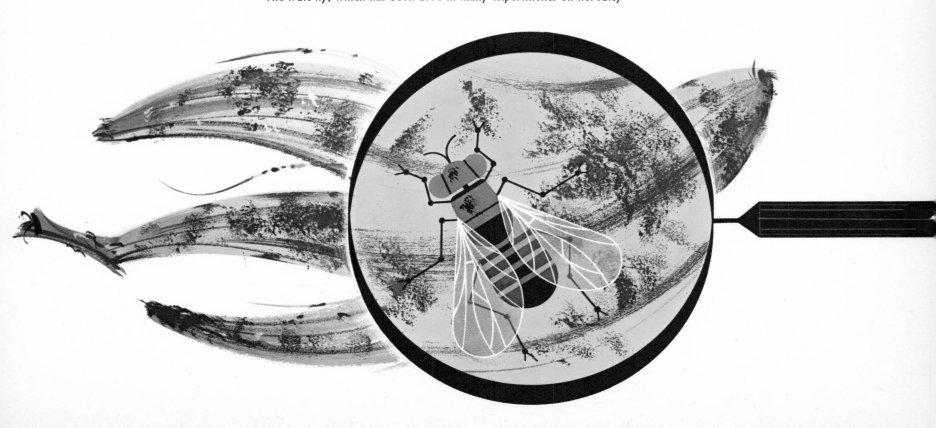

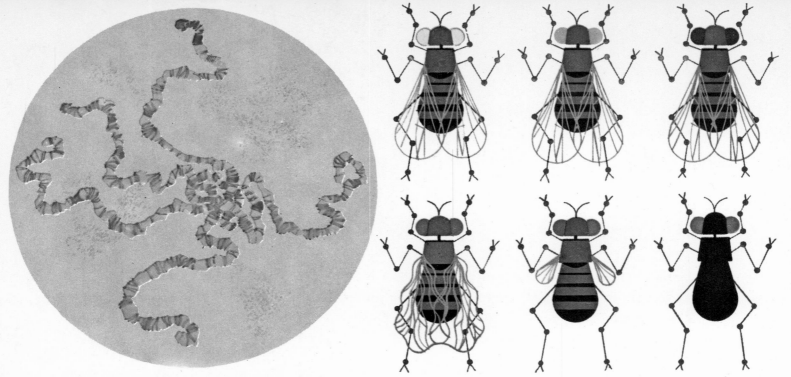

Large chromosomes of a fruit fly, showing bands

Fruit flies with unusual traits

When such a chromosome has been properly stained, it appears to be divided horizontally into a thousand or more bands. What are these bands? Perhaps they show the arrangement of genes along the chromosome. Suppose the genes are like invisible beads strung along many threads lying side by side. Then, even though the separate beads cannot be seen, they add up to give the appearance of bands.

A biology professor at Columbia University in New York City, Thomas Hunt Morgan, began to raise fruit flies in experiments on heredity. For several years he and his students bred flies by the millions. And as Mendel had kept records of many generations of peas, the group at Columbia kept records of many generations of flies, listing all their different traits, such as white eyes and pink eyes.

Once in a while some brand new trait would pop up as if from nowhere. For example, a fruit fly would grow up with wings so stubby that they were useless. Flies with stubby wings were selected and bred, and in this way the scientists obtained a pure line of flies having the new trait.

At the same time, the scientists studied the chromosomes in the large cells of the grubs. When the chromosomes were compared with those of normal flies, a difference was found in the pattern of bands on one chromosome.

This made it clear that the new trait was caused by some change in a gene of the chromosome. The change had first happened in one sex cell of one fly. The altered gene and the new trait were passed on to the young fly that came from that sex cell, and later were passed on to its descendants.

How Chromosomes Copy Themselves

When a chromosome splits and forms two new chromosomes each is a copy of the old. How is the copying done? Since the chromosome is made of many genes strung along one after another, each and every gene must create its own double. Still the question is, how?

This problem has been taken up by biochemists—chemists who study the materials and products of cells. They have found that the chief material of the chromosomes is a complicated molecule called a nucleic acid. One of the atom groups composing it is the sugar deoxyribose, so the molecule is called deoxyribose nucleic acid, or DNA for short. It is formed of two similar strands, which spiral around

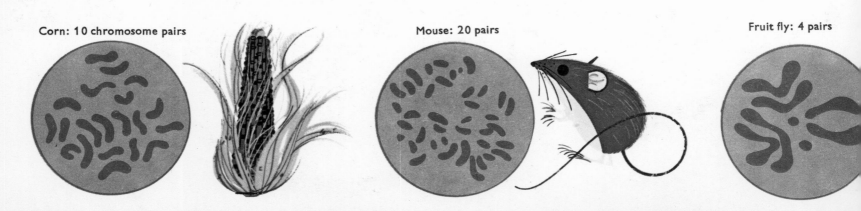

Corn: 10 chromosome pairs

Mouse: 20 pairs

Fruit fly: 4 pairs

one another. Scientists think that the twin strands of a DNA molecule unwind. While this is going on, substances from the surrounding protoplasm line up beside each strand, link together, and form a new twin strand. Since all the DNA molecules of a chromosome reproduce in this way, all the genes are copied and the single chromosome becomes two.

Instructions for Molecules

How do DNA molecules make a creature what it is? How do they guide its growth, cell by cell and tissue by tissue? Scientists believe DNA molecules serve as patterns for shaping molecules of another kind of nucleic acid, called RNA. Then RNA molecules serve as patterns for the making of proteins.

Each kind of protein molecule must be built according to a plan, for it is a very complicated chain, having hundreds, or even thousands, of amino acid groups linked in a precise order. This means that plants for the protein are stored like a code right in the DNA molecules. And the code for a whole organism, with its thousands of traits and characteristics, is packed into the fertilised egg cell from which the organism begins! The cell is of microscopic size; a single DNA molecule cannot be seen even under the microscope. And yet, tiny as they are, DNA molecules provide the blueprint for a cabbage or an oak tree, a mouse or a man.

When the egg cell divides, its code is copied in the genes and chromosomes of the two new cells. This happens again and again in all the cells of the developing embryo. Thus every cell, when it is formed, receives a complete set of instructions that "tell" it what to become and what to do.

You carry the code for *you* in each of the fifty thousand billion cells in your body. Through the code, you are given everything that makes you a human being. And you receive all the particular traits— the features of your face, body and brain—that make you the person you are.

Human being: 23 pairs

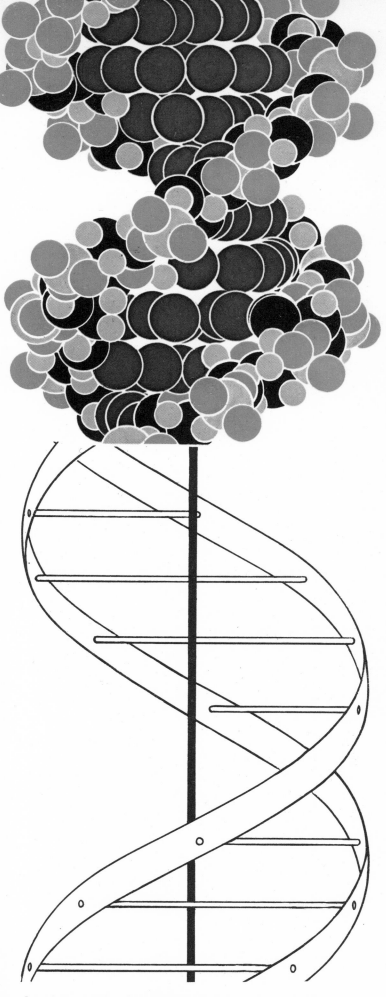

Structure of the DNA Molecule. Two strands made of sugar and phosphate groups wind around one another. The strands are joined horizontally by groups called bases

63

New Kinds of Creatures from Old

Two hundred years ago explorers were coming home with tales of strange plants and animals they had seen in far away lands. Sea captains were sending specimens by the hundreds to a Swedish naturalist, Carl Linnaeus, to be studied and named.

Until the time of Linnaeus, no one had ever tried to list all the known kinds of living things. This would have been a hard job, because the names of many creatures were confused. Often a single plant or animal had several different names, or several different creatures had the same name.

To make things simpler, Linnaeus gave each known kind of plant and animal a scientific name. The wolf, for example, was named *Canis lupus*. The word *Canis* is Latin for dog. As part of the wolf's name it means that he belongs to the group of dog-like creatures. *Lupus*, wolf, is simply the name of the wolf's own kind, or species.

When the coyote became known, it was given the name *Canis latrans*, barking dog. As you can see, this system does more than just name living things. It groups similar species together.

After Linnaeus died, more and more kinds of plants and animals were discovered, and naturalists added them to the list of species. The list grew longer and longer. Was there any end to the number of different species in the world? Where did they all come from?

Why So Many Kinds of Living Things?

At first, nearly everyone believed that each species had been created separately a few thousand years ago. Then scientists who studied the earth and its rocks began finding signs that life is much older than that.

Most of the upper rocks lie in layers, one upon another. A complete set of layers would be many miles thick. The layers were formed of mud and sand that settled on ancient sea beds and later hardened into rock. All this could not have happened in a few thousand years. It took hundreds of millions of years.

In the rock layers, many fossils were discovered. You know what fossils are—traces of ancient living things. Most are casts and imprints made by shells, bones, or other parts of creatures that were buried under the sea.

As scientists went on studying rocks and collecting fossils, they saw that ancient life was very different from that of today. To begin with, the earliest fossil creatures were all sea dwellers. In their times, no plant grew on land; no animal stirred. The continents were bare, lifeless deserts.

After a long stretch of time, living things appeared on land, but they were not at all like any that exist now. Instead of trees and grasses, there were strange marsh plants. Instead of birds and mammals, there were creatures like huge salamanders. Millions of years later, dinosaurs appeared.

As more and more fossil creatures were found, an amazing fact became clear. Today's million kinds of living things make only a small part of a vast, unknown number of species that have existed since life began on the earth.

How could all those millions of species be explained? A French naturalist, Jean Baptiste de Lamarck, wondered about this. He could not believe that each of the earth's millions of plant and animal species, past and present, arose by itself, without any relation to others.

Lamarck had gathered a collection of fossil sea shells. He noticed that some of them—snail shells, for example—were very much like the shells of creatures that live in the sea today, while others were quite different. The shell collection seemed to hint at some message, if one could make it out. Fascinated, Lamarck arranged the shells side by side, with similar ones next to one another. And he saw that they made a series from ancient to modern, with only small differences between any two neighbouring shells.

This could not be accidental, Lamarck thought. Perhaps, in a certain ancient species, small changes occasionally appeared. As generation followed generation, these changes added up, until descendants

Age of mammals
began 65 million years ago
Age of reptiles
began 230 million years ago
Age of early life
began 600 million years ago

Young Charles Darwin in the Galápagos Islands

of the old species became entirely new species. Such development of old species into new is called evolution. Lamarck supposed that evolution is still going on today, but too slowly for us to notice it.

What causes a species to change in the first place? Lamarck thought of the effort animals make to get along in the world—to feed themselves, to protect their young, to escape from enemies. Take the giraffe, which feeds from the leaves of trees. Perhaps its ancestors were ordinary, short-necked animals that ate plants growing on the ground. If such plants became scarce, the animals had to reach higher and higher for their food. By reaching and reaching, they stretched their necks a little. The longer neck was inherited by their young. So it went for thousands of years, and giraffes were born with longer and longer necks. At any rate, that was Lamarck's idea of what happened.

Many other naturalists agreed with Lamarck's views on evolution. If a creature gained a new trait during its lifetime, this "acquired trait", they thought, could be passed on to its descendants.

A Great Voyage of Discovery

In 1831 a young English naturalist, Charles Darwin, set out on a great four-year voyage of discovery. When an expedition sailed for South America on the H.M.S. *Beagle*, Darwin was aboard as naturalist. He spent the next five years visiting South American lands and Pacific islands, and made good use of his opportunity to observe their plant and animal life.

Darwin was interested in the evolutionary ideas of his time, so he kept his eyes open to things that often went unnoticed. As he journeyed along the South American coast, stopping at place after place, he saw that animal species of neighbouring areas were very similar. But in regions more distant from one another, the species differed greatly.

Finally, the *Beagle* sailed to the Galápagos Islands, which rise from the Pacific Ocean six hundred miles west of South America. Darwin was not surprised to find plants and animals of these islands differing from those on the mainland. But what

66

astonished him was that even the species of different islands differed from one another.

He began to realise this while collecting specimens of the sparrow-like birds called finches. Often those on one island were unlike those on another island only ten miles away. The same was true of the giant tortoises—the *galápagos* whose Spanish name was given to the islands. Tortoises of neighbouring islands were different enough so that people who·knew them well could look at a specimen and tell which island it came from. What was the meaning of such differences? Darwin was to wonder about this for years.

Why Are Different Species Like One Another?

The voyage of the *Beagle* ended, but Darwin's work had barely begun. Back home in England, he settled down to writing a report on the things he had seen. The facts were easy to tell; explaining them was another matter.

Thinking of the Galápagos finches, Darwin assumed that their ancestors came from the mainland. The birds reached different islands, where each branch of the family lived by itself. In time, the separated branches changed in various ways. Differences increased, until finally the branches became separate species. Then, if a member of one species should meet a member of another, the two were strangers. They could not or would not mate and produce young.

Darwin supposed that every species of plant or animal is changing slowly all the time. So if branches of a species become separated, the branches will, in time, evolve into new species.

But what keeps evolution going? What makes a species change in one direction or another? Darwin considered the work of animal and plant breeders, and he himself began to breed pigeons. Following

Galápagos finches studied by Darwin

the usual method, he selected birds with certain traits, and bred them in order to have these traits in the young.

After this experience, Darwin always kept in mind the fact that breeders produce desired types by continually selecting the breeding stock. Among wild plants and animals also, he thought, a sort of selection must go on. This he called natural selection.

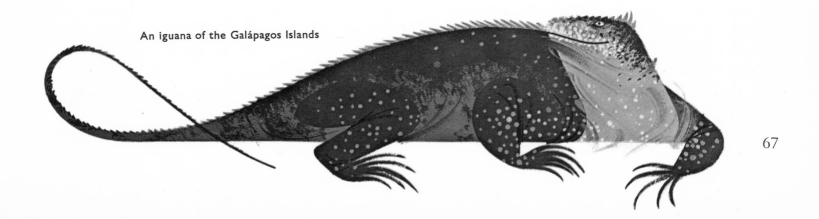

An iguana of the Galápagos Islands

67

We can see how natural selection works by taking a famous example from the past. This is the story of the horse family, which was put together piece by piece as scientists dug up fossils of ancient horses.

The earliest type of horse was a little beast about the size of a fox terrier. It had four toes on the front feet and three on the hind feet. Its teeth, which were low-crowned, were suitable only for browsing on the soft leaves that grow in forests.

A later type of horse was about the size of a collie. Both the front and hind feet had three toes. The middle toe was much larger than the others, and the middle toenail had become a hoof. Later species grew still larger. Their middle toe was long, and the hoof was big and strong. The side toes, quite small and useless, did not even touch the ground. These animals had high-crowned teeth covered with hard enamel. They resembled the teeth of modern horses and other grass-eaters. In ancient times, as now, such teeth were used for crushing tough, gritty stems and leaves of grass.

In the age of the dog-sized horses, forests covered large areas of the northern hemisphere. The horses lived as many other forest creatures did, feeding on soft leaves. But as time went on, the climate of much of the region became drier. Because of this, trees began to die out, and vast forests disappeared. In their place, grasses spread over the plains.

As forest gave way to grassland, what were the leaf-eating horses to do? Some stayed about the same, so conditions became harder and harder for them. If these old-fashioned horses ate grass, it wore down their teeth; then they starved. They did not live long enough to have many young, so finally their branch of the family died out.

Other lines of horses were more fit for life on the plains. These were the big, long-legged types, which could travel far in search of food. Their high-crowned teeth kept on growing as long as they lived. New growth made up for wear, so the animals could feed on grass without destroying their teeth. They lived long and had many offspring. In time, their descendants spread over three continents.

All through the history of the horse family, natural selection was at work. Over and over again, it decided which types would live and which would die out.

The Problem of New Traits

One big question about evolution was still unanswered. What causes a new trait to appear in a plant or animal species? Darwin, like other evolutionists of his time, accepted Lamarck's idea about this. He thought that when an animal acquired a new trait during its lifetime, the trait might pass on to its young.

No one has ever found proof that this happens. A man may have an accident and lose one leg, but still, if he becomes a father, his children are two-legged.

As you remember, scientists have discovered that a new trait is caused by some change in the make-up of a chromosome. Such changes probably happen once in a while in the various kinds of cells in an animal or human body, but there they do not matter much. When they happen in the sex cells, then the changes are important.

In the sex cells as in others, genes and chromosomes copy themselves with wonderful accuracy. And yet, sometimes, they make a mistake. The fruit fly has given us examples of this. One gene in a sex cell of a fly may change. The young one formed from this cell inherits the change, which is called a mutation. And if the new trait happens to be dominant, the fly develops this trait. The change passes on to its descendants. If they breed, there will be a whole line of flies with the new trait—for example, stubby wings.

In nature, such "mistakes" happen only once in a while. But biologists have a way to make them happen more frequently to laboratory animals. Using fruit flies, for example, they shoot a stream of X-rays through the flies, and wait for them to breed. When the young and later generations are examined, they show many more than the normal number of mutations.

This gives us a hint how mutations happen naturally. Small amounts of radiation similar to X-rays are always coming to the earth from space. Perhaps such rays are the cause of many mutations.

The effects of big mutations are bad. Some cause the young of a plant or animal to die when they are just embryos. Others prevent the young from growing up, or from having young of their own. Most

Fossil ancestors of the modern horse

smaller mutations are also harmful. We might expect this. If a species has thrived in the world for thousands of years, it has passed the test of natural selection. Its genes are good, and any change in them is likely to be for the worse.

Yet once in a great while there is a mutation that happens to be useful. Among the horses of long ago, for example, there were mutations towards stronger teeth and longer legs. Lines of horses with these traits multiplied and spread, while lines without them died out. In other words, helpful mutations were preserved by natural selection, and this shaped the evolution of the horse family.

The same process, working through hundreds of millions of years, has led to enormous changes in the earth's families of living things.

Creatures that lived in the sea about five hundred million years ago

Long Journey to Land

For two thousand million years, the sea was the only home of living things. The earliest creatures were microscopic, and for ages their descendants remained tiny. But they did not stay the same. As time passed, some evolved into quite new types of organisms. One line became the soft-bodied animals with shells, whose modern descendants are the mussels, oysters, and snails. Another line became the joint-footed animals, whose descendants are the crabs and lobsters. Still another line developed a backbone and became fishes.

Through all their changes, these various families remained sea-dwellers, for they were fit only for living in water. Yet, in one way and another, a few branches of the sea's plant and animal families found their way to the strange world of the land.

The Difficulty of Living Out of Water

It is remarkable that any ancient sea-dwellers could survive out of water even for a day. Consider the life of their modern descendants who still live in the sea. The tiniest of them breathe through membranes that envelop their whole bodies. Larger creatures breathe through the membranes of their gills, through which dissolved oxygen from the water is taken in, and carbon dioxide and other waste materials pass out.

If a water-breathing creature is cast up on land, it can survive for a while, so long as its skin or gill membranes stay wet. Then oxygen from the air dissolves and passes into its body, and carbon dioxide passes out. As the membranes start to dry, fluid seeping from inside the body keeps them moist. But the seepage continually evaporates, robbing the animal of the precious fluid it needs for life.

In spite of the danger of evaporation, a few kinds of gill-breathing and skin-breathing animals manage to live out of water. One of these is the snail, which breathes through its skin. In dry weather, the snail retreats into its shell. The garden slug, a snail without a shell, gets some protection from its coating of slime.

The earthworm, another skin-breather, would quickly dry up if it spent the day above ground. Instead, it hides in the safe world of the soil. The air in the spaces between soil grains is so moist that it cannot hold more water vapour, so no moisture evaporates from the worm's skin.

Land crabs breathe through gills which must stay wet. Moisture escapes from them, but the amount of evaporation is small, because the crabs stay in burrows and other damp places. At egg-laying time they return to the sea, for their young hatch as tiny swimmers just like the young of other crabs that never leave the sea.

Certain relatives of the crabs do much better as land-dwellers. Turn over a stone and you will probably see a few small, oval-bodied creatures scurrying for cover. These are wood lice, also called sow bugs, though they are neither lice nor bugs. They are cousins of the crabs and lobsters, and like them have a shell like a little suit of armour.

A wood louse breathes through tiny sheets of tissue extending from its underside. These are gills, which must stay moist to dissolve oxygen from the air. If the air is dry, the animal keeps losing fluid. But it is safe so long as it rests on a surface having the slightest film of moisture. The wood louse is good at finding moist surfaces. From them, it absorbs water through tiny passages in its underside. When drought comes, a number of individuals may crowd together. This reduces the surface area through which they lose water. It seems that behaviour, rather than bodily fitness, enables wood lice to live on land.

Modern creatures that breathe through skin or gills. The upper five belong to the sea snail group. Beneath them are: a garden slug, two land snails, wood lice, and a land crab

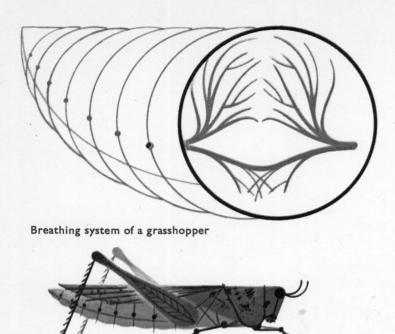

Breathing system of a grasshopper

First to Leave the Sea

Insects are distantly related to crabs and wood lice, belonging to the great tribe of joint-footed creatures. The insects do wonderfully well at living on land, in spite of a serious handicap. This is their small size, which gives them a relatively large surface through which water may be lost. But the insects protect themselves. They secrete a waxy material that coats their bodies and almost completely stops the escape of water.

For breathing, an insect has a system of fine branching tubes. The ends of the tubes go right into the tissues, so that oxygen reaches the cells directly and carbon dioxide passes directly out. The tubes open through breathing holes lined up along the body. These work as trap-doors, closing to reduce evaporation.

The fossil record helps to explain why insects are so well fitted to live on land. They and their ancestors have been land-dwellers for a few hundred million years—longer than any other animals. They have had plenty of time to evolve and become adjusted to life out of water.

We don't know exactly what the ancestors of the insects were like. But whatever they were, they could not have migrated to land suddenly; no water-dwellers are able to do that. Most likely, they were crawlers of the mud flats, who lived as fiddler crabs do today—half the time in the water and half the time out.

Several kinds of plants had already left the waters and grew around bays and lagoons. The earliest known shore plants were little branching stems without leaves. Later, plants developed leaves and root systems. Some evolved into tree-sized ferns, club mosses, and giant horse tails, which covered the swamps with a dense green forest.

With plants growing on land, there was food for the joint-footed animals or any other migrants from the sea.

Castaways with Backbones

Today, fishes still make up the majority of the backboned animals, and most fishes still dwell in the sea. You would hardly expect them to come ashore. And yet, long ago, some fishes did. The proof is that backboned animals who are their descendants live on land today.

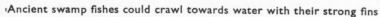

Ancient swamp fishes could crawl towards water with their strong fins

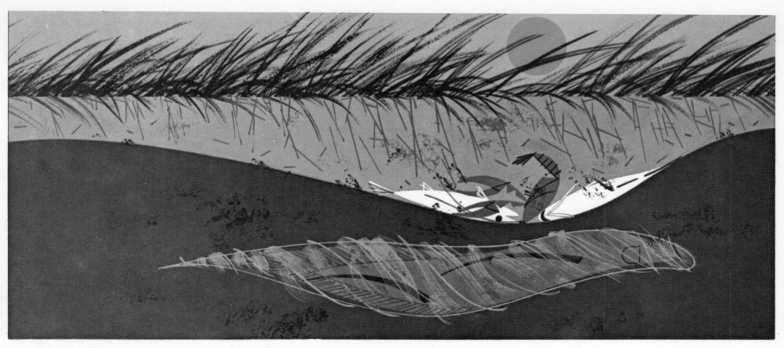

A modern lung-fish can live in mud during the dry season

How did ancient fishes manage to stay alive out of water? A few modern fishes can do it for a while, when necessary. These are the lung-fishes, so named because they have lungs as well as gills, and breathe air as well as water. In fact, lung-fishes would drown if they couldn't breathe air.

The lung-fish Protopterus inhabits rivers of central Africa. These rivers dry up at times, leaving pools full of rotting plants, which deprive the water of oxygen. But the lung-fish doesn't suffocate, it comes to the surface and gulps air. In fact, the creature always breathes more air than water, for its gills are too small to take in much oxygen from the water.

When trapped in a shrinking pool, the lung-fish burrows into mud at the bottom. Drying mud imprisons it, yet the animal is safe. Mucus oozing from its skin dries and forms a protective capsule around it. The fish may lie in its capsule for several months, breathing air and nourished by its fat. When the rains come and water again fills the pool, the prisoner swims to freedom.

Over three hundred million years ago probably all the bony fishes had lungs and breathed air. This was fortunate, considering the places where they lived. Picture a world of great marshes that often shrank and dried up during seasons of drought. Fishes of the swamp waters were able to keep alive at such times, thanks to their lungs.

The swamp fishes had another advantage—four strong fins growing in the position where modern land animals have legs. The fins were set on muscular "lobes". When a fish was left high and dry, it could use its lobe fins to crawl about in search of water. But these fishes never settled on land. They were just stranded there now and then.

73

Battle of the Tyrant Kings. Two Tyrannosaurus dinosaurs fighting over a dead Triceratops

The Double Life

Swamp fishes gradually changed. Among some lines, the lobe fins became larger and stronger and finally developed into legs. These were strange creatures—four-legged, but otherwise fishlike and living mainly in water. But they were not fishes; they were the first amphibians. This name means "leading a double life"— on land as well as in the water.

Today there are just a few kinds of small amphibians in the world: the salamanders, the frogs and toads, and wormlike creatures called caecilians. An amphibian such as the frog is covered with a thin, moist skin, through which it does much of its breathing. On land, the skin is kept moist by water seeping from inside. But just so much fluid can be lost; then the frog must get into water or die. Once submerged, it rapidly soaks up water through its skin. This is the way a frog takes a drink.

Most amphibians lay their eggs in water. This means the young must begin life as tadpoles, breathing through their skin and gills. As they grow, they develop lungs and legs, which help them to make their way on land.

The ancient amphibians probably also laid their eggs in water, and the young hatched as water-breathing swimmers. For them, life in the swamp waters must have been very uncertain. When pools evaporated and rotting vegetation poisoned the water, young amphibians died by the millions.

Backboned animals become better fitted for life on land

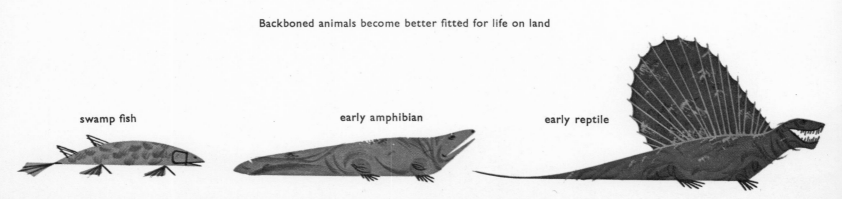

swamp fish   early amphibian   early reptile

The Egg with a Shell

In time, certain descendants of the amphibians developed a large, shell-covered egg. This egg could be laid on land, for the shell prevented it from drying up. The embryo inside had a special membrane that worked as a lung, taking oxygen from the air.

Because the egg had a large yolk, well supplied with food, the embryo could stay inside and grow for a long while. When it finally hatched, the young one had lungs and legs and was ready to live on land. In addition, it had a dry skin, which prevented any great loss of fluid by evaporation. This creature with the shell-covered egg and dry skin was no amphibian. It was the first of a new family, the reptiles.

Since they could breed on land, reptiles began to leave the swamps and settle on dry ground. They spread farther and farther over the continents. Thousands of generations lived and died, and many new kinds evolved. The greatest of them all, the dinosaurs, became kings of the earth. This was a mighty triumph, and to what was it due? Mainly to the large, shell-covered egg, which at last freed backboned creatures from the water, bringing them to the end of their long journey to land.

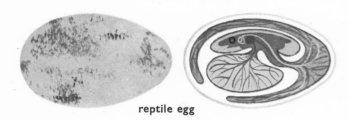

reptile egg

dinosaur

75

The earliest mammals were small. They resembled modern shrews and hedgehogs

Cold-blooded, Warm-blooded

The reptiles' age of glory was long, but finally, around sixty million years ago, it came to an end. The great dinosaur lines had died out one after another. Smaller reptiles remained, but they no longer had the land to themselves. Two new types of creatures were taking over their territories. These were birds and mammals, both descended from ancient reptile lines.

The early mammals were little creatures resembling the modern hedgehog. Scientists recognise them from their skull bones and teeth, but of course these do not tell everything about them. We suppose they were hair-covered and nursed their young with milk. Both the mammals and birds, if they resembled the kinds living today, were warm-blooded. This was something new in the world. The other backboned animals—the fishes, amphibians, and reptiles—were cold-blooded, as their descendants are today.

Cold-blooded Animals and their Problems

You already know something about this matter of body temperature. A bird or a mammal stays about the same temperature all the time. Its body is usually warmer than the air, so we call it warm-blooded. But a fish, frog, or snake warms up or cools off according to the temperature of its surroundings. Its body is usually fairly cool, so we call it cold-blooded.

You can easily find a cold-blooded animal to examine. Take the common housefly. On a warm summer day it buzzes around merrily. But in the chill of autumn it becomes so sluggish and helpless that you can pick it up easily.

The fly is lively on a summer day because warmth speeds up its body chemistry—its metabolism. It burns food rapidly, and this gives it the energy to buzz about. But when the weather is cold the fly is cold too; this slows down its metabolism and takes away its energy.

Reptiles, too, behave according to the weather. When it is warm, their metabolism is quick. Food burns faster in their cells, giving them the energy to be active. When the weather turns cold, their metabolism slows down, making them sluggish.

In autumn, reptiles escape the cold by crawling into underground nooks. There they settle down to hibernate—to pass the winter in a sleepy, sluggish condition. Though seeming half dead, they will survive if they have managed to crawl deep enough. If not, the frost will reach them and turn their hibernation places into graves.

The Warm-blooded Live Faster

Birds and mammals have their metabolism wonderfully well controlled by hormones. These substances pour into the blood stream from various glands, enter the cells of muscles and other tissues, and set the enzymes to work burning food.

When a bird or mammal is active, its hormone and enzyme system speeds up; when it is quiet, the system slows down. But even during sleep, its metabolism never slows down beyond a certain rate. This is called the basal rate of metabolism.

Have you ever had a basal metabolism test? If so, you know how doctors measure the rate of metabolism. They find out how much heat your body pro-

duces while you are resting. This could be done by putting you in a heat-measuring chamber, but it would be too much trouble. Instead, you just sit quietly and breathe oxygen through a tube for eight minutes. The rest is mathematics.

It is known that a human being produces 4.8 calories of heat per litre of oxygen consumed. (A litre is about a quart.) Therefore, the amount of oxygen you use during the test shows how much heat you produce. This is divided by the surface area of your body. The final result is given in calories per square metre (about a square yard) of surface per hour. The figure will be somewhere around sixty calories. This is your basal rate of metabolism.

Similar tests have been given to many kinds of animals, from elephants to humming-birds. Their rates of metabolism, it is found, vary according to size. The smaller animals metabolise faster, the bigger ones more slowly. The humming-bird uses,

Small birds and mammals use more oxygen for their weight than large ones

humming-bird

pygmy shrew

10

common shrew

5

water shrew

harvest mouse

0

pigeon

white rat

monkey   dog   man   bull   elephant

1   2   4 6 8 10   100   1,000   10,000   100,000   1,000,000   10,000,000

WEIGHT IN GRAMS OF ANIMALS TESTED   (28.35 grams = 1 ounce)

Humming-bird: sluggish at night, lively by day

Bat: lively at night, sluggish by day

Woodchuck: active in summer, asleep all winter

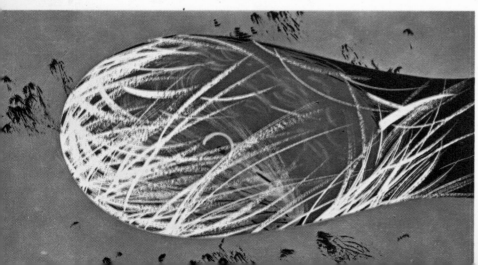

per hour, a hundred times more oxygen per gram of body weight than the elephant. This means it burns about a hundred times more food for its size, and generates about a hundred times more heat. In short, it lives a hundred times faster than the elephant.

The humming-bird's size helps explain why it needs a speedy metabolism. Being small, it has a large surface for its volume, and this means it loses heat rapidly when the air is cool. The bird makes up the loss by producing heat rapidly.

The humming-bird must feed almost continuously in order to keep up its speedy metabolism. This is possible during the day, but what is to happen when darkness prevents it from gathering food? If it functioned at top speed all through the night, the humming-bird would starve. It escapes this fate in an extraordinary way, for a bird.

At night, after the humming-bird has settled down, its metabolism slows to one-fifteenth of the daytime rate, and its temperature drops to that of the air. The little creature sits chilled to the point of helplessness. You can pick it up, just as you can pick up a fly on a cold autumn day. The humming-bird remains sluggish until morning; then its metabolism speeds up to the daytime rate, and it flies about sipping nectar, the fuel for its rapid living.

The Half-death

The bat goes through changes like the humming-bird's, but in reverse. During the day it stays hanging from its cave wall or ceiling, asleep and very nearly as cool as the air. At dusk its temperature rises to a hundred degrees Fahrenheit or higher, and it leaves the cave to hunt night-flying insects.

When autumn comes and no insects are to be found, the bat goes into the deep sleep of hibernation. This is its way of doing without food. With its metabolism slowed down, the bat needs little energy, so it can live through the winter on its fat.

If you ever go exploring caves in winter and find bats there, don't disturb them. If they fly about, using up energy and fat, they may starve before spring.

The brown bear, famous as a hibernator, does not go into so deep a sleep as many others. His temperature falls only about half-way to freezing point.

And he is likely to wake up for a while and feed right in the middle of winter.

Another well-known hibernator in North America is the woodchuck. In summer he busies himself eating and getting fat. Then he is just as lively as any animal his size. His temperature is a hundred degrees, and his heart beats eighty times a minute.

In autumn the woodchuck rolls up in his burrow and begins the long winter sleep. His heat output slows down, his temperature drops, and his heart gives only about five beats or less a minute. At this rate of functioning, the well-fattened woodchuck can sleep and stay alive for half a year.

Squirrels, hedgehogs, and several other warm-blooded animals also escape starvation by hibernating. But the winter sleep has its dangers, for the sleeper may never wake up. It has been said that while a bird flies thousands of miles to escape winter, a hibernator often goes to the very door of death.

As a rule, the sleeper manages to avoid death. A hibernating bear, woodchuck, or ground squirrel will get just so cold, then an internal alarm clock wakes it up. The animal moves about and feeds, and goes back to sleep in safety.

The Built-in Climate

Since reptiles and amphibians depend on heat from outside their bodies, they get along best in the tropics. Few snakes, frogs, and lizards are found in regions where winters are cold, and there are none in the Arctic. But climate doesn't matter so much to birds and mammals. They have a warm climate of their own built right into their bodies. Their system of controlled metabolism makes it possible for birds and mammals to live where winters are cold. The snow owl, musk ox, and polar bear are quite at home in icy lands of the North.

A controlled metabolism was not always as important as it is now. For several hundred million years, before the age of reptiles and during it, the earth's climates were mild. Temperatures did not vary much from season to season, so cold-blooded animals could remain active all year long. In addi-

tion, plants grew throughout the year, so there was plenty to eat.

But there came a time when winter temperatures over vast areas became too cold for reptiles. This change probably killed off vegetation upon which plant-eating reptiles fed. The plant-eaters starved by the millions. Flesh-eaters that hunted them also went hungry and died out. All this did not happen everywhere at once; first it happened in one region, then in another. When temperatures dropped too low, cold-blooded animals must have had trouble moving about. Perhaps a chilly dinosaur would lie stiff and helpless, like a fly on a cold autumn day. It was too big to hide and hibernate, as do many small reptiles of today.

Cold did not harm the birds and mammals. Their controlled metabolism kept them lively, so they were able to move around and take care of their needs. While the great reptiles were dying, the little warm-blooded creatures multiplied, spread, and became lords of the land.

Creatures of the North have a warm climate inside them

Brains and Behaviour

You have spent many years of your life growing up and learning how to take care of yourself. Your parents and teachers have helped, but you yourself must do the learning—and it is work!

By comparison, animals seem to have an easy time of it. Most kinds receive little or no training, yet they get along in the world. As you look into the lives of different creatures, from worms and insects to birds and mammals, you find they are expert at taking care of themselves. How do they manage it? Why is their behaviour so right, so well suited to their needs?

A Worm Can Learn

Consider the earthworm. Its behaviour is not very complicated, nor its intelligence very high, yet at times you would almost think it clever. Have you ever tried hunting them at night? You tiptoe along until your torch beam falls on a glistening worm stretched out in the grass. Since it lacks eyes and ears, it should be easy to catch. You grab for it, but all you get is a handful of grass. The worm has shot down its hole to safety.

How did the worm "know" you were there? Did it feel the ground shake from your footsteps, or did it sense a faint warmth from your light?

In each of its many divisions, the worm has a little bunch of nerve cells with fibres going out towards the skin. The nerve bunches are connected by a cord running through the body from end to end. This apparatus is the worm's burglar alarm. It picks up a signal such as a temperature change or vibration. The signal starts a chemical reaction in the nerve endings. An impulse shoots through them to the nerve bunches. Quickly, a message goes out to all parts of the worm, causing it to pull away from danger.

At the worm's front end, the nerve cord loops around its mouth. Part of the loop is thickened into a nerve bunch bigger than the rest but still very tiny. This is the worm's brain.

The earthworm's nerve cord—an alarm system

How clever is a worm? It does what is right for it, but automatically, "by instinct". Because it carries instructions for wormlike behaviour coded in its genes, it can act without thinking, as its ancestors have always acted.

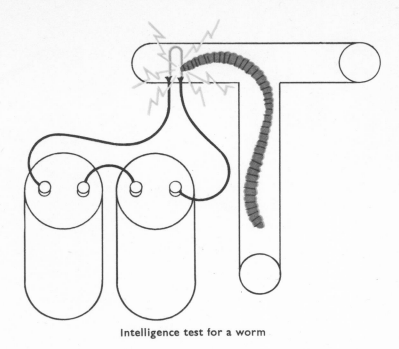

Intelligence test for a worm

Does a worm ever need to learn anything new? For that matter, can it learn? To find out, a scientist thought up an intelligence test for worms. He built a tube—an artificial worm-hole—shaped like the letter T. In a test, a worm was placed in the tube opening, and would start crawling. When it reached the crossing, it could turn either to the right, where the passage was safe, or to the left, where there was wiring that would give a slight electric shock.

The worm began by taking one route as often as the other. Day after day it gave itself shocks, repeating the same old mistake. The worm seemed unable to remember and benefit from experience. But, after many trials, it began to take the good route more often than the bad. The worm had learned!

The Wise Yet Foolish Wasp

An insect like the wasp, bee, or ant can do more things than an earthworm. It behaves in more complicated ways because it has a more complicated body and special sense organs.

The common paper-making wasp or hornet, which takes long flights after food and nest-building material, has enormous eyes. These help it to find its way. Two antennae are useful for picking up the odours of food and the scent of fellow wasps.

In autumn, frost kills all male and unmated female wasps. But there are some mated females which have crept into rotted logs or other shelters to hibernate. When spring comes, each female crawls

out into the light again and starts building a nest, where she will be "queen".

The queen gathers bits of wood and chews them into pulp. With the pulp she begins to build a paper nest on a branch. At first it is just a little cluster of chambers, in which she lays eggs. Grubs hatch from them and develop into female workers. The queen continues to lay eggs, while the workers feed the new batches of grubs, and also take over the job of building. Soon the nest is as big as a football.

These activities are so well organised that you might suppose the wasps planned them. But their behaviour is instinctive and automatic. An unfamiliar situation spells trouble, for then a wasp has no instructions to tell it what to do. When a scientist shut up a worker wasp with a grub but no food, the worker bit the grub in two and offered the hind end to the front end.

Wasps build a nest without being taught

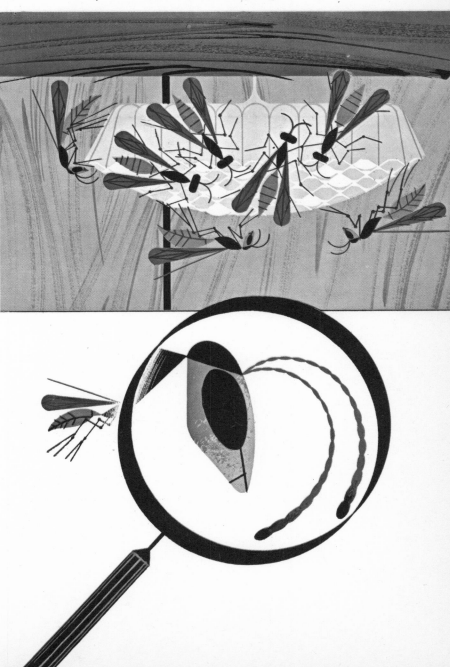

The cuckoo's egg is often found in the nest of another species

Coming to backboned animals; we find that the behaviour of many of them is still largely instinctive. A reptile like the loggerhead turtle gives us an example. Young turtles start out in life without having parents to learn from. They never know their own mother, for she just buries her eggs in the sand and goes away. Little turtles hatch from the eggs, look around at the world, and know what to do. They crawl off towards the brightest light and find their way to the sea, which will be their home.

Intruder Birds

Among warm-blooded creatures, we find more complicated behaviour. That is because they have more highly developed brains, and because their nerves and brains work faster.

Birds give their young ones excellent care, but instinctively and without thinking about it. This is shown by a curious event which sometimes takes place in a family of birds. Once the eggs are in the nest, a bird of another species may surreptitiously lay one of its own eggs among them. In Europe the cuckoo does this; in America, the cowbird.

The intruder's egg is bigger than those of its hosts, but that doesn't seem to matter. All the eggs are incubated together, until there is a nestful of, say, little pipits and a bigger cuckoo fledgling. Soon the cuckoo pushes the young pipits out. They fall to the ground and lie there dying of cold and hunger, but the parent seems unconcerned. In the nest there is still a beak gaping, a voice clamouring for food. So the host bird works and works to fill the beak, since this is what its instinct commands.

Newly hatched loggerhead turtles find their way to the sea

What a Deer Must Know

A new-born mammal—even a mouse—has a large brain for its size. But at first the brain is hardly used, since it is even more unfinished than the rest of the creature. It is like a radio or television set before the wiring has been connected. The nerve cells and fibres are there, but many kinds of connections have to be made between them. This will happen gradually, as the young animal develops. The unfinished state of the brain leaves room for future learning.

A new-born rabbit has the instinct to suck, but can do little else. A fawn is not quite so helpless. It manages to stand or kneel when nursing from its mother. While she is away, it lies still under the cover of grass or shrubs, without knowing that this is the way to hide from enemies. At first it acts according to instinct, but soon the fawn will have adventures in the world, and will learn from them.

A young fawn lies hidden, in safety

Sometimes a fawn has the unusual experience of being adopted by a human being, who feeds it from a bottle. To the fawn, this person becomes mother. It follows the foster mother, and other people, too, as if they were a herd of its own kind. A young deer that grows up in this way can never be turned loose to live in the wild. Unable to tell an enemy from a friend, it would probably walk right up to a hunter, or to a wolf. It would be killed before it ever had a chance to learn the ways in which wild deer protect themselves.

In the wild, a half-grown fawn is led by its mother to the herd. Following her, it follows the herd, and does what the older animals do. When they see or scent danger and run, the fawn runs. Thus it learns to recognise danger and save itself; thus it is trained for life in a dangerous world.

Training for Young Lions

Young lions need more extensive training, for they are hunters, and hunting takes skill.

If you have ever raised a kitten, you know how this little hunter develops. Instinctively using its keen eyes, strong muscles, and quick nerves, the kitten plays with pieces of string and other such "toys". It is clumsy at first, but improves with practice. The more you play with it, the faster the kitten learns.

When a kitten grows up under its own mother's care, with brothers and sisters, it has playmates to tumble with, and an adult to show it how to get along in life. The mother catches a mouse and brings it to the kittens. Soon they are pouncing on it, learning what a cat hunts, and how.

Wild lion cubs are like big kittens, and they go through similar training. At first it is all play. They stalk and pounce on one another, or on their mother's twitching tail. Later they follow her, watch as she hunts, and try it themselves. They make a lot of foolish mistakes, but gradually become more skilful. Step by step, learning is added to instinct.

The young lions' training lasts about a year and a half, not because they are stupid, but because there

Young lions learn as they play together

84

is so much to learn. They must know where and what to hunt, and how to stalk big grazing animals in order to get close enough for the final rush. While in training, the young lions form the habit of working as a group, and will hunt by team-work for the rest of their lives.

The Creatures with Hands

The most complicated behaviour of all is found in the family of creatures with hands—the primates. These include the lemurs, monkeys, and apes. As we know from fossils, the earliest primates were small tree-dwellers. No doubt they used their hands skilfully in climbing around after fruits, nuts, and birds' eggs. Modern lemurs still live in this way. A lemur grasps a branch by crooking his four fingers around one side and his large, strong thumb around the other side.

A monkey, being more nimble than a lemur, does a great deal of jumping and leaping. For this, he needs good vision. His eyes are placed in the front of his face. Since each looks at the same thing, the monkey sees it sharply and clearly. He can tell how far away a branch is, so he knows where to jump.

Monkeys are sociable. They travel in bands and seem to need one another's company. Because they chatter as they go through the trees, each can hear where the others are, even if he cannot see them. So no monkey gets lost, and the band stays together.

Many million years ago, a certain line of monkeys gradually became big and broad-chested, lost their tails, and evolved into apes. These creatures were too heavy to run and jump around, monkey-fashion. Instead, they hung by their arms and swung from branch to branch. This gave them the habit of keeping their bodies in an upright posture.

Before long, the apes divided into two quite different lines. One line developed very long arms and hands, which helped them in swinging themselves along. When an ape hung from a branch, he crooked his fingers around it. This left the thumb sticking out underneath, where it was useless or even a nuisance. In time, the thumb became quite small compared to the hand. All the modern apes have this kind of thumb and hand, for they are descended from the expert swingers.

The ring-tailed lemur grasps a branch with his hands

Monkeys travel in bands

The gibbon—expert swinger, poor runner

The other line never became so expert at swinging. This may be one reason why they left the forest and made their home on the ground. Their feet, unlike the hand-shaped feet of the swingers, became more suited for walking and running. But their hand was old-fashioned, like the lemur's. It had a strong thumb that could bend in and work with the fingers. You know what such a hand will do. Pick up some object like a pencil, and notice that you hold it between your thumb and fingers. The ground apes

A strong thumb helps in handling tools

had hands like yours, and could pick up sticks and stones and use them as tools.

The ground apes divided into several lines, all having an upright posture, feet that were really feet, and hands like ours. In time, line after line died out until, finally, only one was left. This line became the ancestors of man.

The Long Childhood

We shall never know the whole story of the rise of humanity, but we can understand an important secret behind it. Three things go together to make this secret—a big brain, a long period of childhood, and protection of the young by grown-ups.

When we compare the different primate groups, we see that a big brain and high intelligence are connected with slow development of the young. Even before birth, the creature with the better brain develops more slowly. An unborn lemur is carried by its mother for four months; a monkey, five months; a chimpanzee, seven and a half months. A human baby is carried by its mother the longest of all—nine months.

After birth, as before, the different primates develop at different rates. The lemur walks in a few days, and is grown-up in a year. The monkey walks in a month, and is grown-up in three years. The chimpanzee doesn't walk by itself until it is six months old, and isn't an adult until the age of eight.

It is important for a young chimpanzee to have a long childhood under the care and protection of adults. At birth, a baby chimp can only suck and grasp. It clings tightly with hands and feet to its mother's body. If it doesn't find her breast, she takes it gently and places it there. She often cuddles the infant, and sometimes tickles it, making it wriggle and smile.

Other animals may train their young without thinking, just by doing what they always do. But a mother chimpanzee deliberately teaches her infant. When the baby is about three months old she gives it stretching exercises. Lying on her back, she takes its hands and feet in hers, lifts it in the air, and gently pulls its arms and legs out straight. Soon this exercise becomes a lesson in standing. The mother uses her hands to hold the baby's feet against her chest,

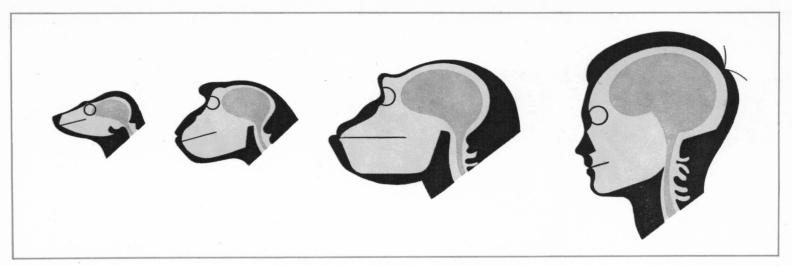

Brain of the lemur, monkey, ape, and man

and with her own feet takes the baby by its hands and pulls it upright.

Month after month the baby's training goes on, until it has learned to crawl, walk, climb, and swing. But the little chimp still needs care. When frightened, it runs and clings to its mother or some other adult. For several years it will need the protection of adults while growing and learning how to take care of itself.

Of all creatures, the one that takes longest to de-velop and grow up is a human child. And no wonder, considering the many things a child has to learn. After crawling and walking comes speech, the skill that makes thinking possible. Hundreds of words, thousands of ways of using them, must be understood, remembered, practised. New lessons and experiences make new connections between cells in the brain. Development of the brain goes on and on, as it must, to permit storing of all the knowledge needed by a human being.

A baby chimpanzee must be cared for, protected, and taught

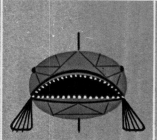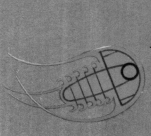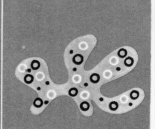

How Did Life Begin?

Have you ever wondered how the first living creatures came to be? At one time this question did not seem very puzzling. People believed that worms sprang from mud, so they thought it quite possible that early living things also came straight from lifeless matter. This notion had to be given up when it was found that even the lowliest creatures have parents, grandparents, and great-grandparents.

As biologists say, "All life comes from life". But if this is so, where did the very first living things come from?

Scientists have examined fossils, gathered clues from chemistry and astronomy, and tried to put all the facts together in a theory of the origin of life. This theory is like an unfinished story, for many parts are missing or doubtful. As scientists learn more about the chemistry of cells, they will surely be able to fill some gaps in the story.

The Raw Materials

The fossil record shows that earlier plants and animals were less complicated than later ones, and that the farther back we go in time, the simpler they were. A few hundred million years ago, all creatures were sea-dwellers. Still farther back, none were larger than single microscopic cells. Beyond that the record stops; we do not know what came before the cell. But there must have been something. A cell, with its protoplasm and many structures, is a very complicated system. It could not have sprung suddenly from lifeless matter, any more than a worm could spring from mud. The cell, and protoplasm too, must have had simpler forerunners.

Today, protoplasm is composed largely of the four common elements, carbon, hydrogen, oxygen, and nitrogen. They make up 99% of the weight of protoplasm. As you remember, plants get these elements from air and water. In the plant cell, carbon atoms are linked in chains, and atoms of the other elements are joined on to the chains to make sugar, fat, and protein molecules. Such carbon-chain molecules are called *organic* substances. In nature today, they are found only in living things and their products. But was this always true?

simple sugar molecule

When scientists try to imagine how life arose, they go back into the early history of carbon, hydrogen, oxygen, and nitrogen. This is the starting point of a theory worked out by the Russian chemist Alexander Oparin. He suggests that the first carbon-chain molecules—the first organic substances—were produced many millions of years ago from four gases which probably made up the earth's early atmosphere. These were methane (marsh gas), water vapour, ammonia, and hydrogen. Methane was the source of carbon atoms; water and hydrogen supplied hydrogen atoms; oxygen came from water; nitrogen came from ammonia.

The American scientist, Dr. Harold Urey, added

to this theory, and one of his students, Stanley Miller, thought of a way to test it. When he was working with Professor Urey at the University of Chicago, Miller experimented with a mixture of the four gases. He set up two flasks, one above the other, with tubes connecting them. Water and the gases were put into this apparatus. When the water was boiled in the lower flask, steam rose into the upper one and mixed with the other gases. Some of the steam condensed into water droplets, in which molecules of the other gases were dissolved. Droplets trickled back into the lower flask and more steam rose. So it went, round and round. Since it takes energy to link simple molecules into more complicated ones, an electric circuit was arranged to discharge a spark through the droplets as they passed down through the connecting tube.

After the first day, the water in the lower flask turned pink. By the end of a week it was red. When tested, it was found to contain various compounds of carbon, hydrogen, oxygen, and nitrogen. Among them were several amino acids, the units of which protein molecules are built. Here was proof that chemical forerunners of proteins could have been formed in an atmosphere of methane, water vapour, ammonia, and hydrogen.

Stanley Miller's Experiment. From a mixture of four gases, Miller obtained amino acids, forerunners of proteins

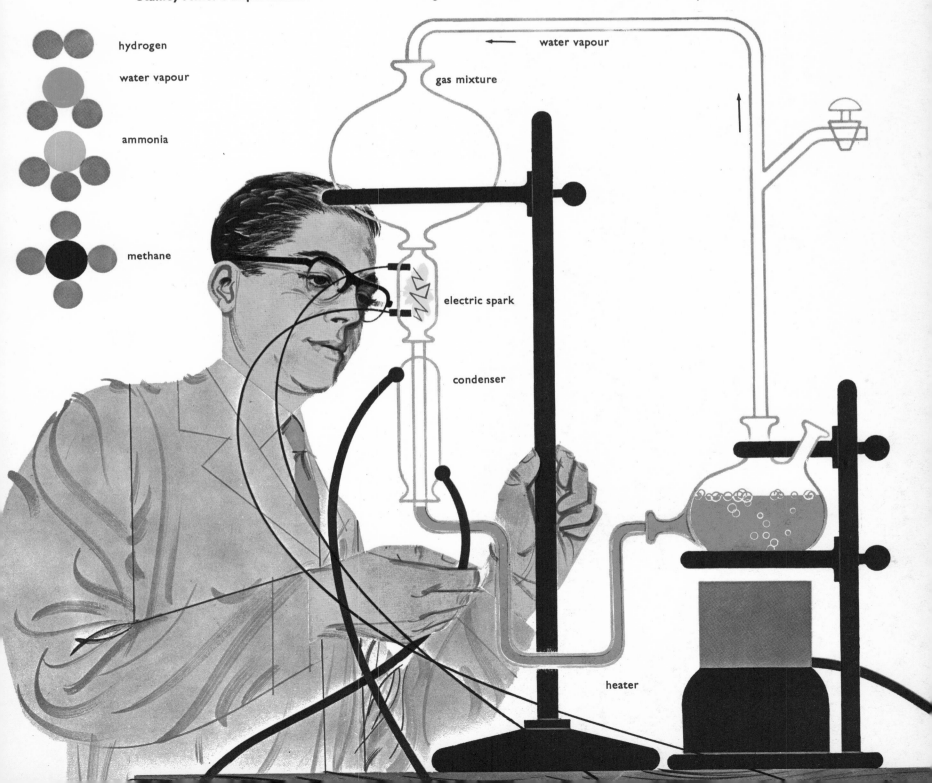

hydrogen

water vapour

ammonia

methane

water vapour

gas mixture

electric spark

condenser

heater

Earliest Days of the Earth

What grounds are there for supposing that such an atmosphere ever existed? This question takes us into the problem of how the earth began.

Most astronomers think the earth, the other planets, and the sun were formed about 5,000 million years ago from an enormous cloud of gas and dust that was drifting in space. According to this theory, gravitational attraction pulled material of the cloud towards the centre. The in-flowing gases formed a great whirlpool, just as water forms a whirlpool when flowing towards a drain. Centrifugal force produced by the whirling made the cloud flatten out into a shape like a huge wheel. Meanwhile matter in the centre of the wheel formed a sphere. Compression of material in the sphere made it so hot that it began to glow, and became the sun.

In various parts of the great wheel, eddies of gas and dust formed whirlpools circling the sun. Nine of these whirlpools were the beginning of the nine planets. They circled the sun in various orbits, some near, others farther out in space.

Hydrogen had been the main element in the original cloud, and was the main element in the whirlpools. Its great abundance affected other elements. Hydrogen united with oxygen to form water vapour, with carbon to form methane and with nitrogen to form ammonia. Where temperatures were right, water vapour, methane, and ammonia condensed into liquid droplets and ice crystals.

In the third orbit from the sun travelled the whirlpool that was to become the earth. As it spun around, some part of the whirlpool was always turning toward the sun and warming up, and another part was turning away and growing cold. Where it was cold, water vapour and other gases formed droplets that coated specks of dust with moisture. When specks collided, they sometimes froze together, forming lumps of muddy slush. Lumps met and merged, and in this way larger and larger masses formed. Finally, most of the solid matter gathered in the centre of the whirlpool, building up a body that became a planet. Inside it were buried the liquids and ices which had frozen the lumps of matter together.

Meanwhile, the freely drifting gases of the whirlpool had been driven away into space by radiation

Gases from volcanoes probably formed the Earth's first atmosphere

from the sun. If this picture of the earth's origin is correct, the new-born planet had very little atmosphere. It lacked rain-clouds and rain, and its whole surface was dry, rocky desert. Yet the earth held a promise of better things to come. It held the liquids and gases that had been locked in the lumps of matter. From this buried treasure would come both an atmosphere and an ocean.

The First Atmosphere and Ocean

In trying to picture how the earth gained its sea and air, scientists consider volcanoes and the materials they pour from the planet's interior. Lava shoots up in liquid or pasty masses. The explosive that blasts it to the surface is a mixture of gases, and the principal one is steam. Some of the steam, it is

thought, comes from water that was buried in the planet long ago while its substance was accumulating.

Quite early in its life, no doubt, the earth grew hot inside, partly from compression and partly from atomic energy. Deep rock melted, and its store of water vapour and other gases dissolved in the mixture. Volcanoes opened up, and exploding steam blasted clouds of rock dust and vapours into the sky. The steam and other gases spread around the planet, forming an atmosphere.

Steam condensed into water droplets. Soon the first rain pelted the dry face of the land. More steam erupted from the earth, and rain continued to fall. It rained for millions of years. Floods poured down from highlands into great hollows, where seas began to form.

91

The gases in the first atmosphere, according to the theory of Oparin and Urey, were mainly water vapour, ammonia, methane, and hydrogen. It was a stormy atmosphere, torn by millions of bolts of lightning. The sun shone on the tops of the clouds, adding the energy of ultra-violet rays to that of lightning.

Energy from these sources caused the atmospheric gases to act upon one another. The four elements in the gases—carbon, hydrogen, oxygen, and nitrogen—recombined to form simple organic molecules. These molecules were dissolved in raindrops and poured into the growing sea. There they joined, making amino acids and larger molecules.

Great Events in the Sea

On the earth as it is today, organic substances cannot lie around very long without decomposing—becoming "spoiled". Either they are acted upon by micro-organisms or they are oxidised by oxygen from the air. But on the young earth there were no micro-organisms. And if Oparin's theory is right, there was no free oxygen. So organic substances did not decay. They accumulated in the sea. The water became a sort of thin broth—a food that remained unspoiled and uneaten.

The molecules in the broth worked on one another. Carbon chains linked together, forming longer and more complicated chains. Some of these finally combined into molecules like the nucleic acids DNA and RNA, and proteins.

Molecules with the atoms of life rained into the sea

Proteins and other large molecules often touched and tangled together. Since it happens that water molecules gather in a film around proteins, the protein strands were held apart a little. As a result, they formed a network enclosing water-filled spaces. The tangle became a microscopic jelly-like droplet.

Around the surface of a droplet, proteins jelled and formed a membrane, which helped to hold the droplet together. Through openings in the membrane, small molecules passed back and forth, and materials were exchanged between the droplet and the sea.

In some droplets, special proteins developed and began working as enzymes. These speeded up chemical activity, so that large molecules were formed rapidly, and the droplets grew. But a droplet grew just so large; then its membrane broke, and the droplet split in two. After a while the two grew large and split, and there were four. Thus the droplets made more and more of their own kind. Nothing like this had ever happened before. The droplets were something new in the world—they were living protoplasm.

Life Changes the World

As the living droplets multiplied, they used up more and more of the broth. Soon there was famine in the sea. Billions of droplets starved, and survivors had to get along as well as they could on left-overs.

With organic molecules becoming scarcer, certain kinds of droplets died out. Others continued to live and reproduce. Somehow—and this is a big gap in the story—various structures and mechanisms developed in the droplets, and they finally evolved into cells. Some of the cell organisms obtained energy from nitrogen, some from ammonia, others from sulphur. These cells were bacteria. Another kind evolved into yeasts, which obtained energy by fermenting sugar.

Meanwhile, the earth was changing. Volcanoes quietened down; clouds thinned and bright sunlight reached the surface of the sea. A new gas—carbon dioxide produced by fermentation—was becoming plentiful in the water.

Certain microscopic cells developed a new substance, chlorophyll, and became green. Others be-

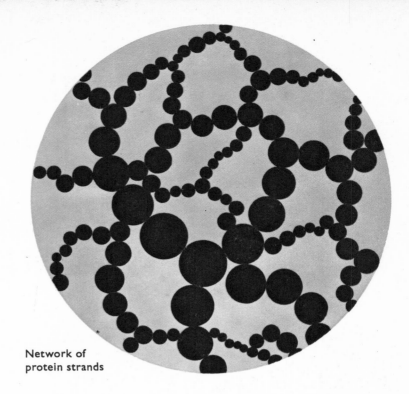

Network of protein strands

came purple, blue, or yellow. These organisms were the first plants. Their coloured matter trapped the energy of sunlight, which split water molecules into hydrogen and oxygen. The hydrogen was linked with carbon dioxide to make sugar. The oxygen was given off as a by-product.

As microscopic plants increased and spread over the sea, they liberated more and more oxygen. The oxygen dissolved in the water and escaped into the atmosphere. There it reacted with the original gases of the atmosphere. Methane was oxidised to carbon dioxide and water. Ammonia was oxidised to nitrogen and water. Gradually, the old atmosphere of methane and ammonia was transformed into an atmosphere of nitrogen, oxygen, and carbon dioxide.

Now that microscopic plants were teeming in the sea, other tiny organisms started to live as animals. Devouring plants and using oxygen to burn the plant food, they produced carbon dioxide, which other plants used.

It was such a chain of events, scientists believe, which led to the life system operating on the earth today. Sea and air were supplied with the gases that ever afterwards would provide the four key elements of protoplasm. Carbon dioxide and oxygen passed back and forth from living organisms to air and water, as they do today. And though the land was just bare rock, the seas harboured throngs of microscopic living things. These were the ancestors of the two great divisions of life—the kingdom of plants and the kingdom of animals.

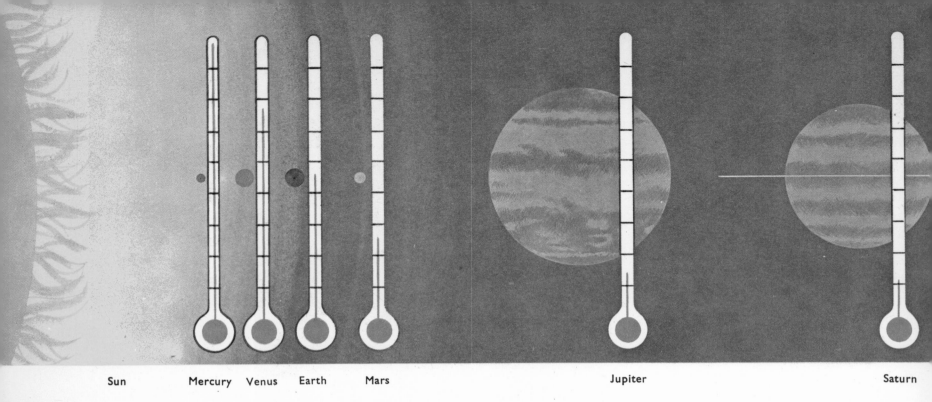

Sun   Mercury Venus Earth Mars   Jupiter   Saturn

Worlds Fit for Life

Looking up at the stars on a clear night, you sometimes wonder if there are other worlds where plants and animals live. Perhaps, somewhere in the vastness of space, there are worlds inhabited by creatures who can walk, talk, and think. Do they, too, look at the stars? Do they wonder if you exist?

The Temperature Problem

If living things exist on other worlds, they are probably made of a watery protoplasm. This could arise only on a world with plenty of water. Temperatures could not be too hot, nor too cold, for if they were, all water would be in the form of steam or ice.

On an ordinary thermometer, the spread between the boiling and freezing points of water looks pretty large, but it would be very small on a thermometer showing the vast range of temperatures in the universe. Stars have temperatures of millions of degrees, while empty regions of space have temperatures more than four hundred degrees below zero.

In our own small corner of the universe—in the solar system—the sun gives heat to all the planets, but more heat to the nearer planets than the farther ones. Mercury, the nearest to the sun, receives so much radiation that its sunlit surface is hot enough to melt lead. The giant planets Jupiter, Saturn,

Uranus, and Neptune, being much farther away, are cold worlds, encased in ice and wrapped in a frozen haze.

Clearly, no living thing could exist either on Mercury or on the giant planets. Mercury is too near the sun; the giants are too far away.

The Right Size for a Planet

For still another reason, life would be impossible on Mercury and on the giant planets. They are not the right size. To be fit for life, a world needs a pull of gravity strong enough to hold the proper kind of atmosphere around it. If it is quite small, its gravity will be too weak to hold gases very long.

Gas molecules are lively things, and this creates a problem. In the earth's atmosphere, the molecules are always in motion, darting around like a swarm of gnats. The molecules of lighter gases move faster, on the average, than those of heavier ones.

The molecules are always colliding. Often one of them gets a shove from another and puts on an extra burst of speed. Suppose this happens high up, where the atmosphere is thin, and there is a lot of space between molecules. A speeding molecule may shoot straight upward without hitting another one. How far can it go?

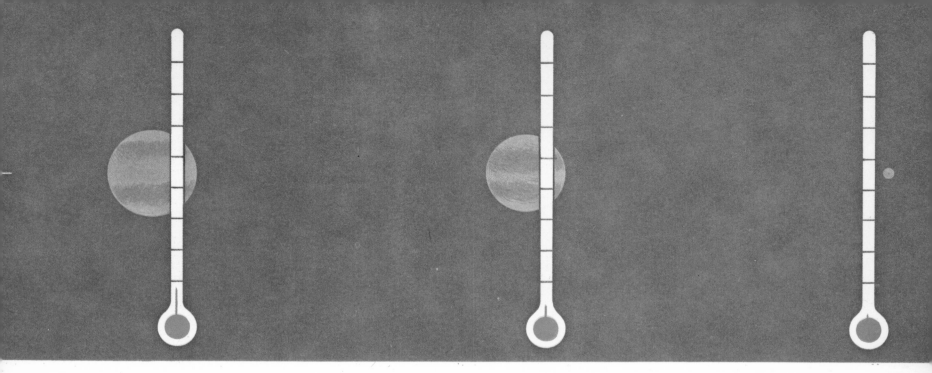

Uranus · Neptune · Pluto

A molecule is like a rocket. On the earth, a rocket shoots into space if it reaches a speed of seven miles a second. This is the "velocity of escape"—the speed at which an object overcomes the pull of the earth's gravity. Molecules of hydrogen, the lightest gas, often reach this speed, so hydrogen escapes from the earth. But molecules of heavier gases, such as oxygen and nitrogen, move more slowly. Hardly any escape, so our planet keeps its air.

On a planet whose gravity is weaker, things are different. On little Mercury, the escape velocity is less than two and a half miles a second. Long ago, many molecules reached this speed and got away. Gases were lost at such a rate that finally none were left. The same sort of thing must have happened on far-away Pluto, and on our moon, for both these small worlds are now airless.

On the giant planets, there is too much atmos-

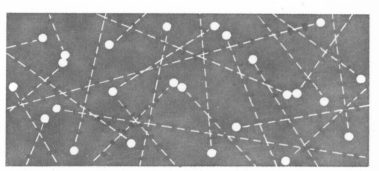

Gas molecules are always darting around

phere. The gravity of a planet like Jupiter is so powerful that it has kept an over-supply of hydrogen. This gas has united with others to make poison vapours that would kill living things. So the wrong kind of atmosphere, as well as icy cold, rules out life on Jupiter and the other giants.

Venus might be expected to have better conditions. This planet, the second from the sun, is warm

Jupiter, with its strong gravity, has kept all its gases. The Earth has lost some. Mercury has lost all

enough. And since its gravity is nearly as strong as the earth's, Venus has managed to hold an atmosphere. There is plenty of carbon dioxide in it, and some water vapour. So scientists do not rule out the possibility of life on Venus. The planet is covered with clouds—probably made of carbon dioxide snow—which hide whatever lies beneath.

Conditions on Mars

Mars, fourth planet from the sun, smaller than the earth but bigger than Mercury, has an escape velocity of three and one-fifth miles a second. In the past, no doubt, gas molecules often reached this speed and got away. Now only small amounts of gases are left, so the atmosphere is thin and sparse.

A landscape on cloudy Venus may look like this

Martian air contains nitrogen, carbon dioxide, and water vapour, but apparently no oxygen. Neither people nor animals could live on such a mixture, but simpler forms of life might thrive on it. Experiments have shown that certain types of bacteria will grow in the kind of gas mixture that surrounds Mars.

Though colder than the earth, Mars is perhaps not too cold for life. In its polar regions temperatures never rise above zero, but around the equator they reach sixty-five degrees. On the whole, temperatures in the Martian tropics may be no worse than in some regions of the earth where life exists. In our far northern mountains, and in Antarctica, there are hardy lichen plants that thrive on bare rock. Something like them might be able to live on Mars.

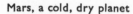

Mars, a cold, dry planet

In Antarctica, lichens grow on bare rock. Perhaps similar plants grow on Mars

No telescope is powerful enough to show whether living things exist on Mars. But with another instrument, the spectroscope, scientists have detected organic substances. These may be signs of life in some stage of evolution. What stage? Perhaps space explorers will find out.

Beyond the Solar System

The ideal home for life, it seems, is an earthlike planet. No other member of the sun's family is quite like the earth, but similar worlds may exist far out in space, circling other suns.

After all, our sun is just one among thousands of millions of stars in the Milky Way Galaxy. And the Milky Way is just one among millions and millions of galaxies. The total of all the stars in the universe is a number so large that it does not even have a name.

With so many stars in the universe, it would be strange if our sun were the only one with a family of planets. It is true no planets have been discovered beyond the solar system. At the distance of other stars, a planet would be too small and too dim to be seen. Yet astronomers think it very likely that other planetary systems exist. They reason that if our sun came from a cloud of gas and dust, other stars came from similar clouds. In many of the clouds, probably, whirlpools formed and turned into planets.

Among such planets may be some about the size of the earth, circling in orbits where they get just enough radiation to give them mild temperatures. Under such conditions, they may have plenty of water, and an atmosphere containing the other raw materials needed for protoplasm.

Step by step, matter evolves according to nature's laws. Once the materials and conditions for life exist, the next step must follow, and it will lead to the creation of the most wonderful thing in the world—matter that lives.

Scientists think it likely that there are some hundred million planets where life could arise. On many such planets, simple organisms may exist. And on some of them, possibly, dwell creatures who can think, and who, like you, imagine they are not alone in the universe.

In every galaxy, there are countless millions of suns

Experimental garden for a space ship. Microscopic green plants grown in a tank supply the monkey with oxygen

Space Biology

In a few years, space explorers will rocket to the moon, and later will visit planets near our own. But before the first expedition takes off, certain biological problems must be solved. One is the problem of an oxygen supply.

Once they have landed on the moon, or on Mars, the explorers will probably find oxygen combined in the minerals of rocks. By proper treatment of the rocks, it could be released. But the problem of oxygen will come up long before a landing is made, since it will take several days to reach the moon, or many months to reach Mars.

Even for a short trip into space, voyagers will need a way to purify the air they carry with them. As they consume oxygen and produce carbon dioxide, something must be done to reverse the process and keep the gases in balance.

To solve this problem, biologists are experimenting with a system like the one that operates on the earth, where plants take carbon dioxide from the air and return oxygen. Special kinds of microscopic green plants have been grown in tanks that are kept brightly lighted. These plants are efficient at photosynthesis, quickly exchanging large amounts of oxygen for carbon dioxide. With such a "garden", a space ship will become a small-scale model of the

earth's system. Plants and passengers together will keep the life-giving gases in balance.

Another problem is: How long can space travellers stand being closed up in a ship? Will they be upset after a while because they have no feeling of weight? So far, astronauts have made only short flights into space. Further experiments are needed to tell how the feeling of weightlessness will affect people over long periods of time.

Before explorers set off for other worlds, biologists must solve these problems of life in space. And they will be solved, thanks to growing knowledge about life on one remarkable planet, the earth.

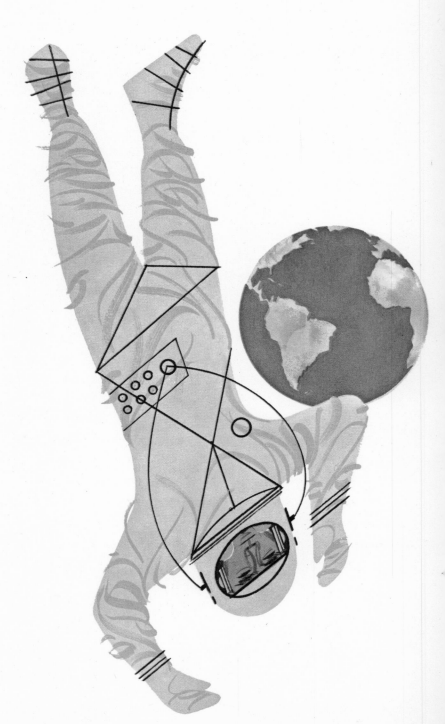

INDEX